D1431506

Survival in Sun and Sand

Other books by Alonzo W. Pond

DESERTS: SILENT LANDS OF THE WORLD

CAVERNS OF THE WORLD

Alonzo W. Pond

SURVIVAL
IN
SUN
AND
SAND

Illustrated with photographs

W · W · NORTON & COMPANY · INC · New York

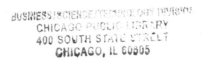
To Dorothy
who survives despite long years
of sun and sand with the author.

Contents

Introduction

Young folks ask the most embarrassing questions of their elders! I recall the story of a sixteen-year-old farmboy who lived near the loess lands along the Mississippi River. Loess is a very fine clay carried as dust from arid lands and river flooded plains by the wind and deposited far from its point of origin. The Mississippi loess deposits probably came from the dried flood plains of glacial streams or the flood plains of the Missouri River. Such deposits are common in China, where they are blown in from the Gobi Desert. Loess weathers into straightsided, canyon-like trenches instead of into sloping-walled valleys.

One day the farmboy's father and his uncle were talking of buying a farm on the loess, "because that land doesn't wash away with the rains like it does around here."

"Then why are the creeks and streams down there so much muddier in the spring than ours are?" asked the teenager. Stony silence was the upstart's answer, but he grew up to write some very important articles on soil conservation.

When I first went to the deserts of North Africa I was impressed by the Roman ruins so common everywhere. Some had been excavated. Beneath the rubble of tumbled walls are beautiful mosaic floors. Some of the buildings had central heating and lead pipe plumbing. I've been down in those two-thousand-year-old cellars and have seen the flues that carried heat to the floors above. Stone-paved streets, elaborate theaters which seated thousands, huge cisterns that still hold water are all evidence of a culture in which food was plentiful and labor for construction abundant. Even slave labor has to be fed in order to do its work.

Every time I mentioned to my guide the contrast between the elaborate cities and farm villas of Roman times and those in the desert today, I got the same response: "Oh, it rained more here two thousand years ago."

Then came the day we crossed a dry stream valley on a new bridge. A few yards downstream there were huge blocks of stone.

"What are all those stones?" I asked.

"That's all that is left of the old Roman bridge," my guide said. "We had a big storm a couple of years ago. It washed out the bridge."

I didn't want to embarrass the older man, so I didn't ask the obvious question. I did think it, however. "If it rained more in Roman times than it does today, how could a recent rain wash out a heavy stone Roman bridge that had been in constant use for two thousand years?" It was two years before I asked the question of an older man. This was M. Albertini, Director of Algerian Antiquities and a well-known Roman archaeologist.

"Do ancient Roman records give any idea of how the rainfall two thousand years ago compared to the average annual rainfall today?" I said.

"Yes, they do," he answered. "The annual average precipitation in Roman times was about the same as it is today. It is difficult to get people to believe such facts."

"Easier to blame the weather," I added, "than to blame human beings for failure to keep water projects in repair when the managers are gone or to follow the rhythm of desert production."

Survival in Sun and Sand will show you details of deserts and desert life today. I hope it will help you to realize that such details are parts of a big picture. Only when you realize that all life is dependent on other life, as well as on the details of climate and environment in that life's tiny corner of the earth, can you really understand what the desert *could be.*

When an explorer finds prehistoric pictures on rock walls showing animals no longer known in that desert region his first conclusion is that the climate has changed. Dr. T. W. Galloway, my science teacher at Beloit College, would be horrified at such a snap judgment.

"A good scientist," he used to say, "collects all the facts, arranges them in an orderly sequence according to their apparent importance, and then draws a conclusion. He must also keep his mind open for additional facts which may change that original conclusion."

It is a popular belief that the Sahara Desert once supported vast herds of browsers and grass-eating animals

Sheep and goats in the Gorge of Saf Saf, Algeria, live on scanty vegetation but must be herded back to water holes.

as well as more people than can possibly live there today. How many who make those statements have taken the trouble to check the population figures for oases in the Sahara? I've seen the general statistics for deserts—so many thousands of square miles, so many thousand inhabitants, equals one or two per square mile.

I once lived in a Sahara oasis. There were three villages in the area that was cultivated. The population density worked out to three thousand per square mile! That compares well with the population density of some of the most industrialized countries of Europe. Why should people who live all their lives and gain all their livelihood from a couple of square miles be statistically assumed to live off thousands of square miles of land that none of them has ever set foot on?

The inhabitants of the oasis where I lived raised dates, garden vegetables, and some grain. Sheep, goats, and camels were brought in for slaughter from distant pastures. Could it be that the animals pictured on the rock walls of the desert were driven out by overgrazing when settled agriculture replaced the hunting tribes? Such changes are still taking place in Africa. Some of the large herds of grass-eaters are found today in areas where the rainfall is not much different from rainfall in once-grass-covered desert.

There are perhaps more questions about deserts today than there are good answers. But such answers will be found when the rhythm of survival in sun and sand is well understood by enough people who are in the desert and of the desert, mentally as well as physically.

What Makes the Desert?

Twenty years ago I used to say that a fifth of the land area of the world is desert. A few years later, scientists working with the United Nations Educational, Scientific, and Cultural Organization (UNESCO) were saying deserts cover a fourth of the land. Now I find ecologists claiming that a third of the world is desert. That doesn't mean, necessarily, that the world is getting drier and deserts are expanding. It does indicate that scientists are more interested in details of arid lands. They are taking a careful look at long-neglected areas. They are trying to learn more about the survival of living things in lands of little rain. If world climate is becoming drier, as some hundred-year records seem to indicate, then knowledge of survival in sun and sand is most important.

Water forms a part of the body of every living thing. Insect or worm, bacteria or bird, the tiniest flower or the giant cactus, the leaping jerboa or the plodding camel, every one of them has water as a large part of its body tissue. Without water there is no life. Although there are many other characteristics of deserts, the absence or scarcity of water is most important.

Once I was flying west over Texas. I saw mile after

mile of green, well-watered landscape. East Texas has thirty to fifty inches of rain per year. Then, as we passed over a large city—I think it was Fort Worth—the landscape changed abruptly. The western edge of the city was definitely West Texas, where annual rainfall drops to fifteen inches. Gone was the well-watered, lush green of the east. In its stead was the dry, dull brown terrain typical of arid lands the world over.

Another time, in western Morocco, we started to fly across the Sahara. Again there were green fields and wooded areas for miles. An hour or so after take-off we saw mountains ahead. The kinds of trees changed as the mountains rose up. Near the crest of the ridge the trees were smaller and stunted. Then, for a few minutes, we could look down on the knife-like top edge of the mountains and see both the east and west sides of the Atlas range. What a contrast!

You didn't need to be a desert geographer to recognize that east of the mountains was desert. West of the ridge the land got water enough for living things from the Atlantic's prevailing westerly winds.

Not all boundaries between deserts and watered lands are as sharp as these examples. Sometimes, as on our flight back from Timbuktu and the Niger River in Central Africa, you could see the scattered vegetation of watered lands gradually become more and more sparse. We watched the character and spacing of the vegetation change. Finally we knew that we were over the driest parts of the Sahara, although there had been no distinct dividing line.

On that southern edge of the great desert the boundary

is so vague that it is best identified by a botanist. Robert Capot-Rey, a French scientist, defined the southern edge of the Sahara as a band, or zone, at whose southernmost points *Cormacula monocantha,* a scrubby thorn bush, grows, and at whose northernmost point *Cram-cram* (*Cenchurus biflorus*), a prickly weed, grows. Another botanist defines the northern edge of the African Desert where the Sahara Plain joins the High Plateau of the Barbary States as the line where alfa grass grows farthest south and the date palm thoroughly ripens its fruit farthest north every year.

The weatherman has another way to define desert. He says that a desert is in rain shadow. That is scientific language for stating that it doesn't rain in deserts. Just as sunlight shadows are heavy or faint, depending on the density of the light-stopping barrier, so rain shadows vary. Also, just as the sun moves around the shadow-casting obstacle, so sneak winds sometimes bring moisture around the obstacle to prevailing winds and give the desert a shower bath.

Oceans are the main source of atmospheric moisture, which becomes rain in the desert as elsewhere. Local evaporation is not very important as a rainmaker. For example, I live in the famous Lakeland Area of northern Wisconsin. There are 800 lakes in 850 square miles.

"Why is the air so dry here?" a tourist asked me. "With all these lakes around I would think it should be damp."

The answer is that our prevailing winds are westerlies. Southwest winds bring moisture up from the warm Gulf of Mexico. Northwest winds coming from the warm Japanese Current in the Pacific sometimes still carry moisture when they reach us. Much of the time, however, west winds blowing across the mountains and the great plains have lost so much moisture by the time they reach us that they are able to hold whatever local evaporation there is from our cool northwoods lakes.

Deserts of the world are either in the path of prevailing westerlies or in the permanent high pressure area of the doldrums, or horse latitudes. It seldom rains in the doldrums, even over the ocean. Those deserts in the path of the westerlies are in the shadow of high mountains. The mountains block the prevailing winds and cause them to drop their moisture as rain on the western slopes. Rarely is there moisture enough left after the air crosses the mountains to produce even a light shower on the desert side.

The westerlies blowing over the cold Benguella Current off the coast of South Africa and over the Humboldt Current coming up the west coast of South America from the Antarctic carry very little moisture, because cold water does not evaporate much moisture into the atmosphere. The westerlies coming across the cold ocean currents simply do not have any moisture to drop on the nearby Kalahari and Atacama Deserts.

Those who use only precipitation to determine desert boundaries generally say that land is desert if it receives no more than ten inches of rain (and snow) per year. Others say less than four inches makes a desert. Some geographers want a still tougher limit and insist that land is not really desert unless at sometime or other there has been a period when no moisture fell for twelve months or longer. Even such a stiff definition will include all the four-inch rainfall areas and most of the deserts with ten inches of rainfall. In addition, there are deserts where no rain has fallen for ten or fifteen years. In parts of the South American deserts no rain has fallen in thirty years of scientific record-keeping, and probably not for fifty years, according to the oldest observers. No matter how dry the desert may be it has rained there sometime in the history of the world. It will rain there again. When it does, the green of some vegetation will appear even though there has been no sign of life during the long, dry years.

Annual average rainfall is valuable for comparison between geographic areas but it seldom tells one what to expect in desert lands. Neither does it show the true conditions to which desert plants and animals must adjust if they are to survive. For instance, in the Namib Desert of Southwest Africa the annual rainfall varies from 1 to 150 millimeters (less than 0.04 inches to 6 inches). The average at In Salah, Algerian Sahara, in 1909–10 was less than 0.6 inches, and in 1925–27 it was zero. One four-year average was 12 mm. (about 0.5 inch of rain per year). In the plant world erratic and uncertain rainfall is as serious a survival hazard as the water shortage itself.

Not only is total desert rainfall unpredictable from year to year, it also varies in quantity and in frequency from one locality to another in the same desert. One study showed a range from no rain to nearly half an inch within a mile and a quarter! When I was on top of Navajo

Mountain in southern Utah I saw four showers pouring rain onto different patches of desert below us at the same time. Each shower wetted only a few acres, and all four of them covered less than 10 percent of the desert I could see. The water was important to the vegetation that received it, but those showers meant nothing to plants on the dry acres between the showers.

A scientist in England, H. B. Rycroft, found that he would need from 9 to 553 rain gauges to get the average monthly rainfall on sixty-seven acres. Even to get the *annual* values on that small area in England it would take from 13 to 31 gauges. In order to get a true record of desert precipitation the gauges would have to be even closer together, because as actual rainfall becomes less the yearly mean variability increases.

In the northern Sahara and Mojave Deserts the rain falls mainly in the winter months. In the Chihuahua Desert of northern Mexico summer rains are the rule, but the Sonoran Desert of Arizona and Mexico has two rainy seasons. Some moisture generally falls there in December and January and again in July and August. Only the summer rain does much good because only then is it warm enough for chlorophyll (green plant material using the sun's energy to produce plant food) to become active.

Desert land also varies in the ability to hold the water that falls in the area. No matter how much rain there is, unless it gets into the ground where it is available to plant roots it has no value to the vegetation. Some desert soil, such as the lee side of a sand dune, is quite porous. Even a heavy rain will sink into the ground quickly. On the windward side of the same dune the sand is packed pavement-hard. An automobile can run across such dune surface, and so will rainwater. Other desert floors are clay. When the clay has been dried out by a long drought and baked hard by months of direct sunlight, a soft, gentle rain may soak down to root-level of the plant life, but a hard rain or desert cloudburst will rush over the surface in a sheet flood until it reaches open cracks in the desert floor or finds a drainage channel, and is lost as far as permanent vegetation on the plain is concerned. Such flood waters will be usable to wadi or arroyo plants for many months after the storm. Of course, if it is long continued, even a torrential rain will soak into the desert a little way and penetrate hard, sunbaked clay. I recall the village of Aoulef Cheurfa in southern Algeria, where I worked for several weeks. All the houses were of adobe or sun-dried clay bricks. On the eastern edge of the village were several ruined houses.

"What happened here?" I asked the sheik.

"Oh, it rained here about fifteen years ago," he answered. "The houses melted so we built new ones where the village is now."

It takes a real soaker to "melt" sunbaked clay, whether it is the adobe brick in a native house or the natural floor of the desert. The first drops of rain cause the clay particles to swell and seal the air space between the tiny grains. Raindrops also act as tiny tampers and compress the clay much as a heavy roller packs the material of a roadbed. It's a wonder to me that any water sinks into the desert plain, even the inch or so necessary to reach the roots of plants, before the water is evaporated by the sun which follows the storm so quickly.

Deserts are "short" on rainfall in all parts of the world but they are very "long" on heat and evaporation. Some controlled experiments have shown that if deserts had a continuous supply of moisture available they would evaporate many times as much as they normally receive. In the Sahara it would take from ten to seventeen feet of rain to keep up with the yearly evaporation. At one rain gauge station, Laghouat, Algeria, the possible loss of moisture by evaporation is twenty-seven times the average rainfall. At El Oued, on the eastern side of Algeria, the possible loss is sixty times as much as actually reaches that area. In contrast to the dry Sahara, stations in Arizona show losses from eight to thirty—or at Yuma, thirty-five—times the average yearly rain. In Australia the loss is eight to ten times and in Central Asia seven to twelve times the available moisture.

Such a great difference between the supply of moisture from rain and the demands of desert evaporation means that desert air and the upper soil are dry most of the time. It also means that every bit of plant life, every insect, every animal, from the leaping kangaroo rat to the swift-running gazelle and antelope, have a constant battle for survival against the desiccation, or drying out, of their body tissues.

Dryness of the air is expressed in percentages as *relative humidity*. The figures represent the amount of moisture in the air at the time of measurement in comparison with the amount of moisture, that air at that

temperature could hold. As the air temperature changes
from cold to hot the figures for relative humidity get
smaller because hot air can hold more moisture than cold
air. When the air gets colder, relative humidity figures
get larger even though no more water has been added to
the atmosphere. As a general rule, relative humidity in
deserts is higher at night and in the cool early morning
than it is in the middle of the day. It is also generally
higher in winter than in summer.

Relative humidity of deserts ranges from 15 percent to
50 percent. It is quite common to find readings of 25 percent to 35 percent. In contrast, at Paris, France, relative
humidity is always over 60 percent. The central Sahara
has several times recorded 4 percent in recent years.
Several years ago that low figure was reported for the
Gobi Desert of Mongolia. It was so unusual that many
meteorologists at that time refused to believe it. Now they
have more accurate instruments, and 4 percent is occasionally reported officially from other desert stations.

When there is so little moisture in the air and seldom
any clouds, the intense heat and light from the sun is not
filtered out before it reaches the desert floor. In the Sahara, cloud cover per year is only 15 percent to 20 percent. Central Asian deserts have twice as much cloud
cover and Paris, France, has about three times as much.
A low percentage of cloud cover, of course, means that
there is a great deal more light available for plants to use
as energy in making food. It also means that more heat
from the sun will reach the earth during the day, but
without the cloud blanket heat is quickly lost into the

upper atmosphere when the sun goes down. Such severe and extreme conditions make survival for plants and animals in the desert a very serious business.

So much of the sun's radiation penetrates to the desert floor that much of it is reflected back into the atmosphere. The air an inch above the bare desert is sometimes thirty degrees hotter than it is a foot or so higher. You can see the heat waves shimmering over a desert plain almost any day between 10 A.M. and 2 P.M., and often for hours before and after that time. The light, hot air at the desert surface and the dense, cooler air above distort the light rays and give us the optical illusion called a mirage, the picture of a lake where no lake exists. Optical illusions, of course, can be photographed, because the camera has an optical lens similar to the lens in your eye. The camera film records the light which reaches it through the lens, regardless of how the light rays have been distorted before they hit the camera.

The clear skies and intense heat at the desert floor which make mirages possible also cause the rapid loss of moisture after a desert rain. The water which sticks to plant leaves or rests on the surface of the desert will pass into the desert air very quickly when the sun shines after the rain. That moisture is lost to the plants. Only that which soaks to root level can be used by the plant.

Fog and dew may be an occasional source of moisture for living things. In the Arabian Desert, close to the hot Persian Gulf, I have seen morning fog so dense that it hid buildings a block away. My friends told me that sometimes fog extended as far as two hundred miles inland from the Gulf. At Tripoli, Libya, I have seen fog heavy enough to prevent airplanes from landing at the airport. On Several mornings in May one year I watched dew dripping off the metal roofs of buildings just about sunrise. Before such dew could soak to root-level of desert plants it was evaporated.

In the Negev Desert of Israel, scientists found small piles of rocks in orderly rows. Each little heap was equally distant from the others. Why would anyone take the trouble to arrange such regular heaps? Finally someone removed the rocks. In several of the heaps they found the dead trunks of grapevines. Obviously the area had been a vineyard a long time ago. The scientists decided that because the rocks would cool off faster at night than the sand and vegetation around, dew would often collect on the rocks and run down to the grapevine roots before the morning sun could evaporate it back into the air. Some ancient gardener had found a way to help his grapes survive the desert dryness a little longer than those of his less inventive neighbors.

There has not yet been enough scientific study to tell us how important fog and dew are to survival of living things in the desert. In such a harsh environment, where the margin between life and death by dehydration is so critical, even an increase in moisture of only a fraction of one percent can mean survival to individual plants.

Dew may give a drink now and then to small birds and insects. Heavy fog and evaporating dew will sometimes lower the stress of heat and dryness for a few plants. But for the desert as a whole, only penetrating precipitation is of much value to living creatures.

2

The Face of the Desert

The desert landscape is flat. Like all generalizations, that statement has many exceptions. There are mountains, and valleys between mountains. There are rolling plains, extensive, flat plateaus, saucer-like depressions. There are isolated peaks from which dry gullies radiate like the spokes of an old wagon wheel. Dry washes are common in all deserts. Sometimes they are called arroyos, sometimes wadis or oueds. There are steep-walled canyons that cut deep into desert plains and expose the flat, layer-cake rock formations that make the foundation of the desert. In some areas there are heaps of sand piled by desert winds five hundred to seven hundred feet high and six times as thick at the base. Sand dunes are the most varied and picturesque feature of the desert landscape, but they cover only a small percentage of desert area.

Despite all those exceptions it is quite accurate to say that desert landscape is flat. When our cars climbed the south slope of the Kingan Mountains and drove through the breach in the Great Wall of China, we stopped on the edge of the Mongolian plateau. There, beyond the grass-

*Wadi Badanah in the Arabian Desert after a flood caused by torren-
tial rains. The modern culverts held, but flood waters raced far
beyond the ancient channel to undermine and cut the modern road.*

ARABIAN AMERICAN OIL COMPANY

lands, the Gobi Desert stretches away north for six hundred miles to the Arctic Divide. It extends one thousand miles east and west. That vast plateau slopes only six feet per mile toward the southwest. At eye level you often see a gently rolling plain but very often we encountered truly level areas stretching to a straight-line horizon broken only by the body of a camel silhouetted against the skyline.

Another time we stopped on the north rim of the Sahara in Africa and looked down on the desert plain. That plain was so flat we could drive standard autos anywhere. Far in the distance we saw a dark splotch on the desert floor. It was a grove of date palm trees. Even though the trees were eighty feet high, all were so near the same height that from a distance the oasis looked like an ink spot on a piece of wrapping paper. We drove for several hundred miles across that plain constantly impressed by its monotonous, flat expanse. Sometimes we saw buttes and mesas ahead but their flat tops only emphasized the flatness of the desert.

When you fly over the desert, even as low as one thousand feet above the plain, you are again impressed by its vast expanse and dance-floor flatness. Once I monitored an Air Force survival exercise on Hamada el Hamra (the Red Plateau) in southern Libya. We flew for miles over a flat area dotted with patches of green. From the air we could see many of the green disks, but the hikers on the ground told me they had seen less than a dozen in their forty-mile walk. The green patches were shallow saucers which collected water from desert storms and held moisture enough for vegetation. Each saucer dipped in a gentle slope only three or four feet below the flat plain, not enough for the depression to show unless a hiker was right on top of one.

It is fashionable for desert writers to insist that the desert was once much wetter than it is now. Of course it was! No part of the earth has always had exactly the same climate it has today. Mountains were once sea bottoms. The northern United States and Europe were once covered by ice a mile thick. When Arctic storms were dumping snow around the North Pole to build up the continental glaciers there was more rain in southern latitudes. Even then desert areas were in rain shadow and sheltered from moisture bearing prevailing winds, as they are today. Despite the abundant precipitation over the northern hemisphere, desert areas got a smaller portion of that atmospheric moisture than the neighboring areas beyond the rain shadow.

In those days, high mountains bounding the deserts and the mountains rising from the plains caught moisture from high clouds. Rivers from those rain-catchers rushed down the mountains and dug channels out into the plain. But their channels and waters never reached the sea. Torrents though they were, they did not cut a route to the ocean.

Along the banks of such old drainage courses in the Sahara there was considerable vegetation. Stone Age people camped along their shores. Crocodiles and catfish lived in their waters. Grass probably grew on the plains between the rivers, as it does today in the Gobi of Mon-

The Bison hunt.

Grasslands of the desert world once supported large numbers of grass eaters.

golia and on the banks of the Niger River in Africa. Animals probably were as plentiful as gazelle herds are in the Gobi or as the buffalo were on the arid plains of the United States. Areas that are in rain shadow get more rain in wet years but never get as much as the non-desert lands. Living things in desert lands must always, sooner or later, adjust to the severity and harshness of the desert.

Ancient drainage channels can be followed far across the deserts even today. The same high mountains still occasionally catch a cloud burst. Then old channels are filled again, to become raging torrents. The rushing waters carry loose rocks and crumbled stone down the slopes and far out on the desert plain. That water-borne debris from the weathered mountains fills in the low places of the desert floor to make it still more flat. Those occasional floods also break the rocks into finer and finer pieces until even the wind can move them farther away from their mountain origin. The accumulated rock debris near the base of hills or mountains is called the talus slope. Floods sweep the talus slopes away from the bottoms of hill and mountains. The result is one of the most pronounced characteristics of a desert landscape. The hills and mountains rise abruptly from the desert floor, almost as abruptly as a building from a city street.

At Tesnou, a granite dome in the Hoggar Mountains of Algerian Sahara, we stepped directly from the flat plain onto the mountain just as we would step onto the porch of a house. The plain was flat as a floor. Several years before our visit our guide had spelled out the name of the mountain with cobblestones. They had not been dis-

Snow-capped mountains, some of the tallest in North America, rise abruptly from the salt pan of Death Valley, which is below sea level.

The Nile at Cairo. The Nile Valley in Egypt is the world's largest oasis dependent on moisture that falls hundreds of miles outside the desert.

turbed. They were not buried in the sand. They seem to emphasize the fact that the face of the desert is flat, despite exceptions like the Hoggar Mountains which rise thousands of feet directly above them.

Only a few desert rivers empty into the sea: in Africa the Nile and the Niger; in the United States the Colorado-San Juan; in Asia the Yellow River. All have their sources in high mountains or regions of heavy precipitation. Each gets such a large volume of water early in its course that it can push through to the ocean even though vast quantities of its water are lost when it flows through the arid lands.

Where these great rivers cross the desert they have been used to irrigate the land. American Indians used the water of the lower Colorado River to grow crops long before the white man reached America. In fact, some students of prehistoric Indian cultures claim that 120,000 to 150,000 people were self-supporting in the southwest desert before the Spaniards killed them off. Their numbers, including natives and Europeans, were not again equalled in the area until 1940.

Of course, the Nile Valley in Egypt is the greatest desert oasis in the world. Waters of that great river come from heavy rainfall in the tropics way up south and flow down north to the Mediterranean. Back in the historic, and even in the prehistoric, past, floods of the Nile spread water and new soil from the tropics over the river's desert banks. The fresh water and new topsoil have made the agriculture of Egypt possible. Only with an abundant and regular source of food from agriculture can a large population survive, whether in the desert or elsewhere.

Modern irrigation systems have carried water from the Nile far out beyond the old flood plains. Hard work and clever use of simple mechanics enable Egyptian farmers to lift the water from the Nile to their fields of grain and cotton. Nowhere in the desert world is there a better illustration of the importance of water. The line between the irrigated fields of Egypt and the dead desert is as sharp as a black line on a white paper.

Short rivers rising in the mountains that border the desert carry water only a little way beyond the mountains before they sink out of sight. In the Gobi and other Asiatic deserts, oases have been established at the mouth of such disappearing streams. At Negrine, Algeria, date palms are planted only three feet deep. They are never irrigated because their roots are in ground water continually supplied by seepage runoff from the Saharan Atlas Mountains. Survival for those trees is greatly simplified.

At El Oued, Algeria, date trees are also planted in ground water, but there is another survival problem. El Oued is in a sand dune area. Although the big dunes are fixed, gardeners have the problem of stabilizing surface sand movement.

In all deserts many of the short streams are channeled into canals to carry water out to gardens and date groves. Even in the days when Rome ruled the world, irrigation works were the basis for the survival of desert agriculture. In the Negev Desert of Israel we saw a series of dams in a narrow canyon that had made several storage basins. In the course of centuries the basins had silted up. Modern

*This irrigating storage basin in a Sahara oasis provides enough
water to sustain productive date gardens, vegetable patches, and
even tiny wheat fields.*

AUTHOR'S PHOTO

power-machinery was moved in a few years ago to dig out the good soil from the basins and spread it over the nearby fields. The old dams were repaired with a little cement. When I saw them, those old Roman structures were back in service doing the job of making the desert bloom as they had done fifteen hundred years ago. They also illustrated how desert flood waters fill in all depressions and make the desert more flat.

Hand-dug wells are the most common means of getting the water necessary for the survival of modern desert inhabitants. In the Gobi such wells are generally only 15 or 20 feet deep. On the plateau Hammada el Hamra in the Libyan desert they go down 130 feet. In the northern Sahara there are artesian wells hand-dug by specialists. Water used to come up to the surface, but when modern well-digging machinery began tapping the ground water supply the old wells had to be deepened.

During the last few years well drillers have discovered "underground lakes" in the Algerian and Spanish Sahara. In Arabia, ARAMCO (The Arabian American Oil Company) has drilled hundreds of water wells for the desert nomads and gardeners. The company has also produced a motion picture, part live and part animated, to teach the Arabs that even artesian wells will not last forever if the valves are left open and the water wasted.

One of the most interesting of desert waterworks is the irrigating tunnel. Wherever such tunnels exist they are a distinctive feature on the face of the desert. In French Sahara they are called *foggara*. In Iran and the Near East they are *quants*. The same system is used in Central Asian

This hand-dug well at Tripoli, Libya, supplies water for the oasis garden.

AUTHOR'S PHOTO

deserts and in Mexico. The system consists of a series of wells extending for miles out into the desert from an oasis. They are easily seen because of the doughnut-like ring at the mouth of each well hole. These doughnut mounds contain all the dirt from digging one well plus half the dirt from the tunnel which connects that well with each of its neighbors. The wells are necessary as an exit for the tunnel dirt and to give daylight to the diggers. Light from each well allows the diggers to see halfway to the next hole. The tunnel, therefore, is dug forward and back from each well. Water from the damp sand around the tunnel seeps to the channel and flows to the oasis, where it is metered out to the gardeners.

Who first discovered the tunnel method of collecting desert water for his garden is not known. When I first saw a foggara it was supposed to be a prehistoric system, "and no one knows how to make it now," my informant said.

I had a map only three or four years old that located a stone-age habitation site in relation to the end of the foggara. With compass and tapemeasure I tried to locate the place. It wasn't to the south, as the map indicated. Perhaps the map maker was confused about direction, I thought, and measured east and north and west. Still no stone-age site. Finally a local man said, "Oh, yes. We lengthened the tunnel about half a mile a couple of years ago."

I went half a mile back toward the oasis and found the site just where the map showed it should be. That same year I saw workmen start digging two new irrigating

The oasis of Aoulef Arab, deep in the Sahara of Algeria, is supplied with water from irrigating tunnels. The water is sometimes carried long distances in adobe aqueducts across low basins to water other basins farther out in the desert.

AUTHOR'S PHOTO

tunnels and later found historic records dating the time of a foggara in Morocco and naming the man who financed it over five hundred years ago.

One of the foggara that I saw being dug was started in a dry riverbed near the Hoggar Mountains in the central Sahara. There were cattails, sometimes called elephant grass in Africa, growing ten to twelve feet high in the old water course. Even though there was no surface water in sight, the elephant grass was a good indication that the diggers would soon have a water-running ditch that they could extend as a tunnel when they worked upstream into the desert plain.

Short desert rivers may end in salt lakes. The most famous, of course, are the Bear, which empties into Great Salt Lake, Utah, and the Jordan, ending in the Dead Sea. The banks of these fresh-water streams support abundant vegetation right to the salt-water terminals. There the landscape becomes salt desert, with sparse plant life or none at all. More often the stream ends in such a shallow basin that its water evaporates and leaves a flat, salty hardpan. Frequently the ancient basin is so smooth and hard that it will support automobile traffic. Sometimes, however, the smooth surface is only a thin crust easily broken. Such salt flats are dangerous traps for men or machines because there is only soft, sticky mud below the crust.

Other shallow, flat basins are intermittent lakes. They may dry up quickly after a storm. One such lake in the Gobi disappeared while surveyors of the Central Asiatic Expedition of the American Museum of Natural History

At In Amdjel, Algerian Sahara, just below the Tropic of Cancer, elephant grass grows eight to ten feet high in the dry riverbed where
water is only three feet below the desert floor. The chief of In
Amdjel, in the right foreground, is riding on a bull, a strange but
sturdy desert mount.

AUTHOR'S PHOTO

were mapping it. In the Kalahari of South Africa rain showers appear to follow a chain of such flat basins. The rain even seems to have "preferences" and falls more often on a few favored playas than on those nearby. Salt pans and playas, dry water channels, and crumbling mountains all supply sand for wind to sweep into dune-filled basins.

Dramatic stories of caravans being buried by shifting sands simply are not true. A sandstorm is not like a snow blizzard. It lasts only as long as the upwind supply of sand can be moved by the storm's wind force. An hour or so is usually enough time for a wind to smooth the edges of a sand supply. Wind cannot "catch hold" of single grains of sand. It can move clusters of grains. Once the sand is moving the wind acts on each grain but movement must start with a cluster.

You can see how true that is if you watch an auto crossing the desert. A dust cloud follows it because the car wheels cut into the smooth desert deeply enough to produce a track. Wind which has been blowing constantly in one direction catches hold of groups of grains on the edges of the fresh track. It quickly smooths off the ridge and no more dust is moved.

Dust is defined as particles so fine or light that once lifted into the air they can be held aloft by shifting air currents. Sand, on the other hand, is quickly pulled back to earth by gravity.

It takes a wind moving eleven miles per hour to move unprotected sand grains along the desert floor. As sand rolls along it gathers speed. When it bumps into a tiny obstacle each grain bounces into the air. The wind pushes it more easily while it is off the ground, so it makes a pretty fair jump before gravity pulls it back to earth. If it falls onto other grains of sand they are splashed up and moved along.

Strong winds may move sand with the force of a sand blast and lift it as high as six feet above the desert floor. A severe sandstorm can make "frosted glass" of an auto windshield or blast off the enamel to the shiny metal. Such storms also carve desert rocks into fantastic shapes. They have cut into the stone faces of pyramids and temples of ancient Egypt. You can see wind carvings on desert rocks more than six feet above the plain today. That carving was done centuries ago before the desert plain had been weathered down to its present altitude.

Any obstacle which slows the force of wind can be shelter for the sand. A rock or even a small pebble can cause the wind to drop the sand and build a tiny heap, a sand shadow pointing downwind. A bush or tree will accumulate sand about its roots, adding protection for them against the heat and dry air as well as making a trap for future raindrops.

As each little sand heap builds up, it too creates an obstacle and more sand is accumulated. Eventually a stronger wind, new eddies around the barrier, or wind from another direction will move the sand on toward low basins where the great fixed dunes have accumulated. Some small, young dunes thus move across the desert. Throughout the world such movement seems to be at about the same rate, twenty feet per year. At that speed it

Small shrubs and animal tracks in the Arabian Desert. The bushes have changed the wind direction and reduced its force so that sand is dropped about the plant roots and protects them against greater loss of moisture.

would take a pretty lazy man to get buried by naturally moving sand.

I have seen abandoned oases where the sand has crept well up the trunks of date palm trees. I have seen isolated buildings partially buried in sand. One village—I believe it is in Denmark—was buried by sand in the course of about thirty years. It was uncovered by the same persistent winds during the next generation. In the case of "buried oases" the explanation seems to be that water shortage caused the few inhabitants to abandon the area. No one was left to sweep away the sand after a storm as we northerners shovel away snow.

In contrast to these few exceptions, there are many, many large, living oases in the very midst of the great sand areas. Great dunes like the Grand Erg Occidental of Algeria, which I crossed on foot and by camel, are fixed landmarks. Maps of the area made 150 years ago are usable today. Our guide recognized specific dunes as readily as a Swiss guide recognizes his Alpine peaks. Throughout the centuries loose sand has been windswept from desert *reg,* or plain, and playa to great basins and large, ancient riverbeds. In a few cases water occasionally flows in the valleys and is blocked, forced out of its course by the dunes. Sometimes the water helps to stabilize the sand and build a permanent dune.

Always there are extensive flat, level corridors among the large dune beds. *Gassies,* they are called in the Sahara, and they are the easy routes for caravans to travel. Occasionally travelers must cross the big dunes, but wherever possible they follow the level gassies.

The wind not only sweeps the plains and the plateaus and the basin floors to fill in hollows and build up obstacles, it also dries the desert quickly after a storm. It dessicates the unprotected plants and animals, another hazard to survival in the land of sun and sand. Above all, however, the wind helps to keep the face of the desert flat.

Such a flat, monotonous landscape, unprotected from full sunlight by a cloudless sky and sprinkled by erratic rains only at irregular, unpredictable periods, is a habitat too severe for plants and animals. Fortunately for living things they are not forced to live in this broad, general picture of the desert. Instead, each living plant or animal of the desert has found a way to survive in a particular corner, a local habitat, where some of those broad, general characteristics of the desert have been modified or are missing. Each living thing survives because it has found a microclimate, a little corner in which the desert is just a little easier on life. Some have found ways to avoid the worst and wait for the best of desert weather just as tourists to Arizona do. Some have been able to create their own environment, like the people of Phoenix, Arizona, with their air-conditioned houses and lawns sprinkled with water from mountain snows far outside the desert.

All desert dwellers, plants, animals, or primitive peoples have somehow found a way to live where nature has provided the minimum of necessities and makes no guarantee of their delivery. They survive on the land of sun and sand.

3

Just Enough for Survival

The preceding chapters give a generalized picture of the desert world. It is a place of uninterrupted daily sunlight and wide daily contrast between heat and cold. Relative humidity is always low. Rainfall is irregular, unpredictable, scanty, or absent for years at a time. There are flat, barren plains, rugged, barren mountains, and hills of sand. This description is an accurate generalization. Fortunately there are exceptions to all generalizations. If there were no exceptions there would be no plants, no animals, no living thing in the world of deserts.

Most people see the desert from man's economic point of view. They see that general picture in which there is a shortage or excess of everything. An ecologist sees the picture in more detail. He sees each plant, each ant or spider on the ground, each bush or tree, each jerboa or gazelle in association with all other living things as well as in relation to the details of the landscape and the microclimate. The ecologist sees the desert from the point of view of nature; in terms of what the characteristics of the area mean for each individual bit of life. Each is in its own little world.

From that point of view, at least one ecologist has said, "There is no water shortage in the desert. There is just enough." Despite the stark reality and true harshness of the desert, each living thing has somehow managed to get just enough of all that it needs to survive in the land of sun and sand.

Where too much sun will kill, each plant or animal finds ways to have just enough. If the water is scarce each finds ways to fulfill its needs. If there is temporarily too much it keeps enough for survival. When food for young birds is limited the adult lays just enough eggs to hatch only as many young as can be fed. In fact, some years one species will not even nest because there is just enough food for the adults.

Some animals, when moved from northern deserts to southern deserts, change their mating time so that their young are born when spring in the new location will supply enough food to nourish the babies.

Just enough for one species may be too much or too little for another. Conditions may be just right for a species for many years. It prospers. But in the course of years or decades the species itself may change the environment. The area may acquire enough food for more individuals, and the species spreads. The changes may leave only enough for fewer individuals of one kind but a suitable amount of everything for some other species. A different species then prospers and is said to crowd out the first.

Such a changing picture has been recorded in photographs of the Sonoran Desert in the southwest United States. Landscapes photographed fifty to eighty years

Our lunch was served in the shade of "The Tree" in the Gobi of Mongolia. The tree makes a small corner of the desert more hospitable and provides just enough more of what small plants need to let them grow despite the surrounding harshness.

The Arabian Desert. When conditions are right there is abundant life, and nature maintains supplies of moisture just large enough to support the life that is there.

ago were recently re-photographed from the original stations. Landmarks are identifiable in old and new pictures.
The new pictures show how much the vegetation has
changed. So far scientists don't want to say positively that
the changes would not have occurred without the inter-
ference of man. Whether those changes are for better
or for worse depends on the point of view, that of man or
of nature.

No space on earth is long barren of life if there is just
enough heat, light, water, and air to support some living
thing. On November 14, 1963, at 7:30 A.M., the skipper of
a fishing boat off the shores of Iceland actually saw a new
island being born in the ocean. Eighteen months and
twenty-five days later the first plant was photographed
on that new island. It was a sea rocket (*Cakile enden-
tula*) whose four leaves contrasted sharply with the
sterile background of the granular, volcanic island surface.

Once I was walking with Dr. Hugh Iltis, the well-
known botanist at the University of Wisconsin. We were
on my scenic boardwalk tourist trail through the sphagnum moss and tamarack swamp here at Wisconsin
Gardens.

"Do you suppose we could bring in other swamp plants
and have them grow here?" I asked.

"Don't worry," said Dr. Iltis. "You already have a great
variety, and when conditions are right others will be
here. There are so many ways for plants to spread into
new territory that you can be certain they will appear
when there is a tiny space with enough of all they need."

Years ago I was boasting to Neil Harrington of the Wisconsin Conservation Department about how many hundred thousands of trees my crew had planted one summer.

"That's fine," said Harrington, "but your fire-fighting work will plant more trees in a season than all your crew could in ten. If we can keep the fires out of the north-woods, nature will reforest it fast enough."

How right he was! It is only thirty years since Harrington said that. The fires have been controlled for a generation in our northwoods. The landscape is green and tree-covered now from horizon to horizon. The forest is growing faster than the paper mills and lumbermen can harvest the trees.

It is the same in the desert. Once in the Gobi we camped on a plateau called Holy Mesa. It was near a Mongol lamasery, and herdsmen kept their herds and flocks away. Grass grew waist-high all over the area. But the plain below, only about fifty feet lower, was barely covered with sparsely spaced clumps of inch-high grass. Flocks of sheep and herds of antelope kept the plain cropped short, but fresh seed from the ungrazed plateau was blown over the plain every year. The grasslands held their own despite intensive grazing, because enough plants were left undisturbed to scatter seeds. Those seeds were ready for the right conditions to produce new plants each year.

In every desert there are exceptions to the general harshness. A rock casts shade over a slight hollow during the midday heat. It slows evaporation of moisture from the last rain long enough for a seed to sprout and set its roots for survival. Water from a heavy shower on a sand dune soaks into a patch of loose sand a foot or so. Above and below that level the sand is dry. An Arab herdsman has seen the rain. He feels the damp sand below the surface to estimate the accumulated moisture. "Enough!" he says. "Enough! There will be a few plants in the dunes to feed my camels."

A heavy rain pelts down on a grassless, level plain. The resulting sheet-flood sweeps to an imperceptible depression. For a few days there is a shallow pool. The water lasts just long enough to create another exception. That small spot in the arid plain is damp. Dry seeds have been swept into the basin by wind and flood. Thousands of them now have enough moisture, soil, light, and air. In a few days that patch of arid plain will be a field of flowers.

A cloudburst explodes with thunder and lightning over the black slopes of a desert mountain. Torrents of water rush down the mountain to fill old river channels. The swift current tumbles rocks and sand along the river bed. Some of that debris piles up at bends, leaving sandbars and stagnant pools when the flood has passed. Another exception to desert harshness has been created. Seeds will sprout. Their roots will grow fast and follow the moisture deep into the earth below the river bed. A tree or bush has found enough of all it needs to start life in the arid waste.

There is more moisture on the edge of a modern paved road across the desert than there is just a few feet away

These trees are a rare sight for the Central Asiatic Expedition in the Gobi of Mongolia. They probably got their start in an unusually wet year, and their roots were able to reach deep moisture before the riverbed dried up.

AUTHOR'S PHOTO

on the plain. Paved road and unpaved plain catch the same shower, but the road-collected moisture is added to the narrow strip along the pavement. That roadside ribbon becomes a world more moist than the general plain only a step away.

Canyons often drain cold air from the mountains above. The lower temperature of the canyon floor is different enough from that of the desert plain to be satisfactory for plants usually found higher in the mountains. Conditions of heat, light, and moisture are so different on opposite sides of a canyon that plants common to the north side are not found at all only a few yards away.

Near sheltering rocks or shade-casting banks, wherever grass or shrubs have found a foothold, lizards, jerboas, and other tiny desert dwellers find enough food and shelter to survive. Large creatures like gazelle or hyenas can move a considerable distance to find shade beneath a bank or can hide among the rocks after they have found their meal. In any case, freedom of movement enables desert forms of animal life to satisfy their different needs from more than one little corner. Unlike plants, their survival is not limited to a single small spot in the desert. They can move to several places which are exceptions to the general harshness.

The desert is harsher for young plants and young animals than for adults. For example, the temperature of the ground where a seed sprouts is much hotter and drier than higher in the air, where branches of a more mature bush or tree are growing. Generally, if the seedling can find enough for all of its needs it will survive to adulthood.

This lone tree provides the slightest change from the harshness of the surrounding Gobi Desert, and makes it possible for a bird to nest and raise its young.

Each plant and animal in the desert has developed different habits or some difference in its physical form or in its body processes from those of its relatives in less harsh regions. Some species have become "look-alikes" in the desert although they are not related biologically. Despite their different origins they have met desert conditions with similar adaptations.

When these adaptations are understood one can say truly, "There is no shortage of life in the desert, there is just enough."

The ancient Egyptians once made paper, papyrus, from this desert reed, Cyperus papyrus.

4

"...May Live to Fight Another Day"

When I was in grade school, fistfights were not uncommon at recess or after school, especially if the teachers were not looking. Sometimes a loser would suddenly depart the battlefield. While supporters of the strong boy shouted "Coward," the loser's friends justified the retreat and chanted:

> *He who fights and runs away*
> *May live to fight another day.*

None of us knew that we were quoting the English writer Oliver Goldsmith, who wrote those lines in 1761. Nor did we know that historians and philosophers have often said the same thing in different ways since 1542.

Those schoolboy lines describe one way that plants have successfully adapted to the harshness of the desert. The plants speed up their life cycle during the few weeks of satisfactory conditions. While the desert is temporarily favorable the plant rushes from sprouting seed to flower to seed again. Like a good general, the plant retreats from the situation it cannot dominate and waits for the chance when its "enemy," the desert harshness, is off guard.

These desert plants are related to the annuals in other parts of the world. But when they grow in arid lands one can hardly call them annuals, because they often do not get a chance to sprout every year. That is why they are known as ephemerals, or "quickies."

The champion quickie was reported in 1920 from the Sahara near Timbuktu by the Danish botanist, O. Hagerup. He said that he had seen a member of the four-o-clock family (*Boerhaavia repens*) scatter seeds eight or ten days after it had sprouted! Several other species of plants had flowered two weeks after the rain. Some were even bearing fruit. However, the *Boerhaavia repens* had the shortest time from seed to seed again.

Generally, the quickies are smaller than their relatives in temperate climates. Otherwise they are easily recognized because they have not changed their characteristic appearance. Their adaptation has really been avoidance of the desert. Their seeds alone have become adapted to take advantage of favorable conditions. These species can scatter mature seeds so soon after a rain that the plant's life cycle is completed before its corner of the desert is back to its normal harshness. The species survives despite the short life of individual plants.

When seeds of desert quickies are taken to non-desert places they still show their quick reaction to favorable conditions. A collection of seeds from fifty species of plants in the northern Sahara was shipped to Denmark for experimental study. There they were planted, and

This Panamint daisy in Death Valley is one of the quickies whose seeds sprout, grow, flower, and scatter seeds before the moisture from the last rain has dried from the desert floor.

DEATH VALLEY NATIONAL PARK

Another quickie from the floor of Death Valley.

DEATH VALLEY NATIONAL PARK

88 percent of them (forty-four species) sprouted in three days. Only 6 percent of similar native Danish seeds sprouted that quickly. Some of the quickies have grown and developed seeds at Grenoble, France, and at Algiers, Algeria. Both locations are in mild, pleasant climates, in contrast to the arid harshness of the Sahara, where the seeds were produced.

In the American Southwest there are about five hundred species of ephemerals. Some sections of the desert floor have as many as five thousand seeds per square yard! When conditions are suitable all five thousand of them sprout at once. More than half of them survive to produce more seeds. Those that do survive share equally in the moisture available. All grow to the same height, which means that limited moisture makes all of them small compared to their non-desert relatives. Probably most of those which do not survive are eaten by desert creatures. They are, at least, not destroyed by competition with their neighbors.

As Dr. Frits W. Went, the botanist and ecologist from the California Institute of Technology, has said, "Among the annuals there is no ruthless struggle for survival between individuals after the seeds have germinated."

Evolution has operated on the seeds. It has produced species capable of survival by controlling the time of germination instead of by adapting the growing plant to the harshness of the desert.

Seeds of many species in the American southwest are able to "measure" the amount of moisture in their area. They also "recognize" whether it has come down as rain or up from below as capillary water. Finally, they are even "time conscious" and will not sprout unless the moisture has come at the right time. Winter-blooming plants will not sprout even if the right amount of rain falls on them at a time when later desert heat would shrivel up the young plants before their seeds could ripen. Summer bloomers will not germinate if the rains come so that the young shoots will not have warmth or light enough for full development.

If the floor of Death Valley, California, is to have a spring flower show there must be more than an inch of rain during the previous November or December. In 1941 Death Valley had a wet year. The precipitation was 4.2 inches, more than three times the normal annual average but not enough of it fell at one time in November or December. *Despite all that water there was no mass of flowers that year or the next.* In the spring of 1939 and again in 1947, as well as in later years, there were literally millions of pink, yellow, and white blossoms carpeting the desert floor. During the November or December preceding those colorful springs more than an inch of rain had triggered the germination of sunflowers, evening primroses, and desert five-spots.

An inch of rain in December on the floor of Death Valley means enough moisture to last the ephemeral seedlings through a comfortable growing season. There will be light enough and warm days enough for the little plants to grow, put out their flowers in March, and set the seeds before the leaves wilt and die.

How does the tiny seed of a desert five-spot resting a

The floor of Death Valley, California, will be covered with colorful flowers in the spring if an inch or more of rain falls in the previous November or December.

DUNCAN M. PORTER, MISSOURI BOTANICAL GARDEN

A bear poppy, one of the plants in Death Valley that will blossom and go to seed if the right amount of moisture comes at the right time of the year.

DEATH VALLEY NATIONAL PARK

quarter-inch below the desert surface know all that? At that shallow depth the soil is just as wet after a quarter-inch of rain as it is after an inch or an inch and a quarter. Also, how can the seed tell whether the one inch of rain was falling in November and not in August or January? Dr. Went and others noticed the four-month lag between favorable rain and flower display. They also noted that the seeds were choosy about the quantity and timing of the rains. Then they began laboratory experiments.

The scientists found that the seeds contained an inhibitor, something that would not let them germinate. They also discovered that the inhibitor could be leached away by sprinkling the seeds with a "rain" equal to an inch and a quarter of precipitation. An equal amount of water applied through the bottom of the seed trays did not carry the inhibitor away. The water had to leach down from the top to remove the inhibitor.

Various seed mixtures were also treated in the laboratory. Summer-blooming species would not germinate in the winter greenhouse. Neither would winter seeds sprout in the summer house.

None of the seeds would begin to grow after a series of short showers when those showers amounted to the critical inch of moisture, unless that total was reached in less than forty-eight hours. It would seem logical that seeds might experience several small showers over a period of dry years. Even though each was not heavy enough to leach away all of the seed's inhibitor it must remove a certain percentage of the supply. One would expect that eventually a last shower would trigger germination at the wrong time. The experiments proved otherwise. Even when the total precipitation from numerous showers amounted to over three feet the seeds would not sprout. Only when the critical inch of moisture fell within two days of proper temperature and proper number of daylight hours would the desert seeds start to grow. Other experiments established the fact that light conditions enable the seed to restore the strength of its inhibitor if some of it has been leached away by rains that are too light.

The rain clouds may be able to fool some of the seeds some of the time. If they do, those foolish ones never grow up. But the wrong rain never fools all of the seeds even once, and so the American Southwest deserts blossom brilliantly every few years.

Dr. Went and his colleagues made another interesting discovery. They found three species of plants growing in dry riverbeds. Paloverde, ironwood, and the smoke tree all have very hard seeds. Left in water for a year, these seeds do not soften enough to germinate. Only a few days after a cloudburst has made a torrent in the riverbed and the water has disappeared out in the desert, the damp stream channel is covered with young shoots. Still more strange, young smoke trees never sprouted under the parent plant. They were always 150 to 300 feet downstream. Why not at 100 feet or 500 feet? How can seeds measure their travels so accurately in a raging flood?

Back at the laboratory, the scientists discovered that the seeds sprouted in water quickly if the hard coat was broken. In the flood waters of a desert arroyo they are ground between sand and rolling stones. That treatment for 150 to 300 feet is enough to break the seed coat. The seed then settles to the muddy bottom to sprout and grow when the flood has passed. If the seed is carried too far, the embryo as well as the hard coat is crushed and damaged so that no growth occurs. This special adaptation of the seed insures that the new plants will grow only where they can be certain of getting enough moisture for their development and being far enough away from the older plants to have the light they need.

James Rodney Hastings and Raymond M. Turner collected fifty- to eighty-year-old photographs of the U.S. Southwest desert and rephotographed the same scenes. When the pictures are compared one easily recognizes many changes in the desert vegetation. Among other differences, one can see that the mesquite has spread over large areas where it was scarce or absent fifty years ago. Why? One reason is that cattle now eat the mesquite beans when they can't get more desirable grass. The seeds pass through the cow's digestive system uninjured and are "planted" on the desert with the cow droppings. Those digestive-softened seeds have a most favored place to germinate in the rich, moisture-holding manure. Also, they are more widely scattered than if they were not carried by the cattle. There are probably other reasons for the increase of mesquite, but the ability of the seed to travel uninjured in a cow's stomach and get itself "planted" in a well-fertilized spot on the desert floor certainly has helped.

Over on the other side of the world is the baobab tree

of the South African arid lands. Its seeds must be softened in the stomach and intestines of a baboon before they will germinate. Perhaps that is why those grotesque trees are so well scattered. They are generally found as isolated individuals, although occasionally several are close enough to each other to be photographed on one negative.

Everyone is familiar with different types of seed dispersal in temperate climates. Some seeds have barbs that catch in the fur of animals or on man's clothing. Others are blown about by the wind. Ralph A. Bagnold, the British scientist who traveled all over the Libyan Desert studying the formation of sand dunes, made an interesting observation about these two types of seed dispersal. He found over most of his desert travels that seeds were generally carried by the wind. Once he found jerboa, or kangaroo rats, out in a barren desert fifty miles from any vegetation. The little animals lived entirely on dry seeds. Their daily dinners were brought to them on the prevailing winds, which carried the seeds into their remote and sterile habitat.

However, when Bagnold got down near the southern edge of the desert, plant seeds were nearly all sticktight or burr-covered. They could cling to the fur of animals and so be carried back into the desert where they belonged. Wind-borne seeds in that section would have been carried out of the desert into a region less favorable to the plant's adaptation.

In many ways it seems that the seeds of desert plants

have developed ways to beat the desert harshness. They illustrate a justification of the philosophy expressed in Goldsmith's poem:

> *For he who fights and runs away*
> *May live to fight another day,*
> *But he who is in battle slain*
> *Can never rise and fight again.*

5

Roots — Water Pipes of the Gathering Field

At pumping stations in the oil fields along the Persian Gulf coast of the Arabian Desert I saw scores of pipes. Farther out on the desert single pipes branched away from the main collection. Each pipe ended at an oil well. Oil from those distant sources was carried back to the pumps through the gathering field. The sight of all those oil lines concentrated in the gathering field near the pumping station reminded me of a tea party we had had years before in the central Sahara.

I was crossing the desert on the first auto caravan to make the attempt after the Citroën Motor Company Expedition from France had crossed with caterpillar track vehicles. We had six-wheelers equipped with pneumatic tires. Three or four crossings had been made by individuals in standard four-wheeled cars, but that news had not made the front pages. Our three-car caravan had all the prestige of an expedition.

About halfway between In Salah and Tamanrasset, Algeria, we met a camel caravan of the desert military patrol. We knew the little French corporal in charge. He and his two native soldiers invited us to have tea. The meeting was on the flat, gravel-covered reg, one of the flattest, most barren stretches of landscape I ever saw.

The Chamba soldiers got out their little teapots, tiny glasses, water from the goatskin bag, sugar, and tea while we chatted with the corporal. Everything was ready except the fire to boil the water. Then I noticed one of the Chamba walking slowly over the plain. He was looking down as if searching for something. I joined him just as he stooped over and started to dig. He had found the stub of a plant. Not more than an inch of dead wood stuck up on the gravel plain. The soldier scraped away sand and gravel for a minute or two. When he could get a good hold on the woody stub he pulled up the plant. That single plant had roots enough to furnish all the fuel we needed to boil water for fifty-two glasses of tea. Desert etiquette requires that each person drink three servings. The gathering field of that desert plant, through which it had collected water, impressed me as much as the oil-gathering pipes had in Arabia.

A desert plant's water-gathering system is an interesting study in adaptation for survival on arid land. No matter what else it does to keep alive in its harsh environment, a desert plant must first get water. Water reaches the plant tissues by way of the root system. What happens to prevent that water from being wasted once it is in the plant is important, but first the roots must get the supply.

The quickies have shallow roots that reach out in all directions from the central stem. Their job is to collect moisture only for the short life cycle of the plant. We

The roots of many desert plants are similar to this gathering field of oil pipes in the Arabian Desert.

ARABIAN AMERICAN OIL COMPANY

have already explained that seed-controlled germination guarantees the needed moisture before plant growth begins. That is why there is no apparent difference between the roots of desert quickies and those of their non-desert relatives.

The problem is quite different for perennial plants. They must somehow stay alive from one rain to the next even if it is months between drinks. If the roots are going to do their job they must be *where the water is* when that water is there. The most certain way to accomplish this is to reach down to permanent water supplies. Some plants have succeeded in doing this even in very dry deserts. Bagnold found at least one rocky corner in the Libyan Desert of western Egypt where desert plants had reached ground water. Among those rocks plants kept alive years after the canyon floors had dried. The explanation is that there is a hard layer of rock not far below the surface. It keeps the water "perched" well above the deep ground-water level. Plant roots reach it and are kept alive for years between desert storms.

When the Suez Canal was being dug acacia roots were found at almost one hundred feet below the surface. Similar deep-growing roots are reported from the region of the Caspian Sea and also near the Dead Sea. In the Caspian Sea basin, roots go down forty or fifty feet. At that depth they strike water and branch out to collect it.

In the Namib Desert of southwest Africa the roots of *Welwitschia mirabilis* reach water in an underground riverbed at forty to sixty feet. A scientist challenged this observation because she had never found roots of that species deeper than five feet. The controversy proves a point more interesting than either observation. The deep roots were in a very dry area in the bed of a channel that had been dry for a long, long time. The shallow roots were in a depression in a flat plain, where heavy mist often condensed. There the ground didn't lose water so fast. This dispute reminds me of the catch question, "How long should a man's legs be?" and the answer, "Long enough to reach the ground." A plant's roots should be long enough to reach the water it needs. The depth of the water, not the plant's species, determines the length of roots.

The mystery is how a sprouting seed gets its roots down such great depths to reach permanent moisture. Some people believe that plants with very deep roots are centuries old. Perhaps their seeds sprouted long before the ground-water level had dropped so low and their roots followed it down. During the 1934 drought in American short-grass prairies, poplar trees growing in riverbeds dried up and died. Their shallow roots had ordinarily found plenty of water between floods. The same species of trees outside the riverbeds survived the drought. Their roots had always reached for deep moisture and had grown down nine feet in only five years. Bur oak (*Quercus macrocarpa*) in that same area also survived, although most other species died off. The oaks had deep roots which reached below the dried-out soil. The deep-rooted trees had never depended on near-surface water but always tapped a deeply buried supply.

Smoke trees which sprout in riverbeds after a desert

Welwitschia bainesi *(called* mirabilis *by its discoverer) in the Namib Desert of southwest Africa has roots that may go forty to sixty feet to water. In this area it is not unusual for ten years to elapse between rains.*

FIELD MUSEUM OF NATURAL HISTORY

flood put out three leaves and stop growing above ground. The roots, however, keep growing until they are in a good water stratum. Then the part of the plant that is above-ground starts growing again. The roots continue to grow five times as fast as the tops. Some other trees—the *pistacia vera* of Central Asia is one—grow five feet of root in one summer. *Aristida pennala* has three to five roots as much as forty inches long three weeks after sprouting, while only a tiny blade of grass shows above the ground.

Seedlings of *Quercus catesbaei* have roots 5.5 inches deep while the shoot still has only two leaves. One plant of *Quercus calliprinos* had a shoot 2.4 centimeters high when the taproot had reached 33 cm., more than thirteen times the length of the green parts. The shoot of a *Dalea spinosa* had roots 40 cm. deep before the shoot was 3 cm. above ground.

Plants with such fast-growing roots can take advantage of available moisture near the surface after a desert rain. They can get *where the water is permanently* before their growth is stopped by arid surface conditions.

Dr. Went points out that some American deserts have quite regular winter rains, but heavy summer storms come only every few years. In those regions desert perennials sprout only after a summer rain. It provides enough moisture to keep the seedling healthy until dependable winter rains take over. That gives the plant a full year to get its roots established. Then it can carry on in drier, normal summers.

Many desert plants depend on scattered showers for their moisture. They can't wait for the rains to soak far below the surface. Evaporation follows too quickly after the rain for much water to soak far down. Also, on dry desert plains runoff is fast. The roots that best serve plants in such locations are those closest to the surface when sudden showers fall. One euphorbia was found to have roots going to a depth equal to only a little more than the height of the bush above ground. However, the area those roots covered was twice as wide as the longest root.

A perennial grass, *Aristida papposa*, was found to have roots extending over an area five times as wide as the above-ground plant but their depth was only four times the plant width. Small grasses an inch or so high may have roots forty inches long.

Rain often soaks deeper around the edges of a plant than directly down from the main stem. In Kenya, on Southeast Africa, one study showed that rain soaked under the plant a distance equal to "the height of the plant plus the depth which it soaked in bare soil." In other words, the plant leaves form a catchment basin and channel the water which falls on them to the roots.

Such root studies are not easy to make. One can't just dig up the plant as we did when we wanted fuel for our tea party. Such a procedure would break off many fair-sized roots and probably all of the tiny filaments. Careful studies are made by gently washing the soil away from around the plant until all the underground parts are rescued.

Only the ends of roots, the growing tips, actually absorb moisture. The older parts carry that moisture back to the plant stem and serve to hold the plant in place. Tiny, single-celled root hairs are so numerous about the root tip that they look like a veil. Each hair is an elongated cell of the root tip. It never grows into a root. Its job is to pull moisture from the soil.

Roots and root hairs reach every bit of soil within their range. You can get some idea of the fabulously complex mass of a plant's roots from a study made on a single plant of winter rye grass. It was grown in a box on two cubic feet of soil. The total length of the roots was two million feet—over 375 miles! There were fourteen billion root hairs. Each day that grass plant produced three miles of new roots and fifty miles of root hairs. With such a rate of growth, you can understand what the florist means when he says a potted plant has become rootbound. Wild desert plants don't get root-bound, but it is necessary for them to reach water where that water is.

Desert travelers frequently notice the even spacing of perennial plants. It is especially noticeable from the air in a stand of creosote bush (*Larrea divaricata*). Each plant is equidistant from each of its neighbors. The distance between plants may be more or less in one desert than in a drier or wetter area, but whatever the distance it is uniform for a stand of the same species.

In Death Valley the bare spaces between the plants are wide. In other deserts where there is more dependable moisture the spacing between plants is not as great, but it is just as uniform. Each plant gathers water from a large surface area with a keep-your-distance root system.

Dr. Went and his colleagues discovered that the roots

secrete a poison that prevents other plants from sprouting. All competition is kept out of the area, which will supply just enough moisture to meet the creosote bush's needs. In regions where rain is heavy the water will leach or wash away the toxic material at the outer edges of each plant's reserved territory. Spacing in such wet areas is much closer than in dry deserts.

Several dry years will kill off the older plants. Generally, five dry years are followed with a year of above-average moisture. The result is that the creosote bush stands are marked by five-year age groups, like a school that took in a freshman class only every fifth year.

Many plants in arid or semi-arid regions store moisture in thickened roots, bulbs, and tubers. These underground parts survive drought even though they are not deeply buried. During the hot, dry season the upper parts of the plant die down. When the rains come, roots, runners, and bulbs all respond almost as fast as the quickie seeds and send up new shoots. Bare desert becomes covered after a rain when these underground parts have survived.

Buffalo grass (*Buchloë dactyloides*), the most important plant of the short-grass prairie from western Minnesota to Arizona and New Mexico, spreads by underground creepers. Each node (joint) on the stem can send roots down and short, narrow grass blades up when moisture is present. In the Judean Desert of the Near East, *Atriplex halimus,* a member of the goosefoot family, also sends up shoots from a creeping rootstalk. More spectacular, however, is the drought resistance of desert-growing bulbs. A bulb of *Leontice eversammi* was collected in Turkestan. It was about the size of a potato. The collector put it on a shelf in the laboratory after weighing it. Three years later it had lost hardly any weight. It had not dried out after thirty-six months and sprouted when it was given proper growing conditions, just as if it had never been subjected to dry air.

No matter how efficiently the gathering field of roots, bulbs, or other underground parts make water available, the rest of the desert plant cannot waste that water and survive. The adaptations by above-ground plant parts for conserving water are sometimes almost too fantastic to believe.

"Waste not, Want not"

Waste not, want not, is a maxim I would teach.
Let your watchword be dispatch, and practice
what you preach;
Do not let your chances like sunbeams pass you by,
For you never miss the water till the well runs dry.

Rowland Howard in Peterson's Magazine, 1876

An apple tree in New York transpires and evaporates 2,166 gallons of water in the 188 days of its growing season. Other trees in temperate climates generally lose 1,000 to 2,000 gallons per year. An annual, like a single cornstalk and its leaves, loses four quarts of water per day. Other grasses have a daily loss equal to their own weight. Such losses are tolerable in temperate climates because there is usually enough rain each year to replace them.

These temperate climate plants, however, could not last long in the desert. Dry desert air day after day after day evaporates many times more water than they would lose in their native regions.

A water-loss study on date palms in the Sahara gives

a good idea of how much faster plants lose moisture in dry air than in temperate areas. Although the date tree is an oasis plant with its feet in the water, its head is in eternal sunshine. It is subject to the same dry air and intense heat as native, wild, desert plants. Every year the date tree evaporates and transpires 42,268 gallons of water. That is 19.5 times as much as the New York apple tree.

Obviously desert grasses, annuals, wild trees, and bushes couldn't tolerate comparable water losses. The desert rains just do not supply such quantities. That is why true desert plants have used every conceivable way to "waste not" the water their roots have gathered. No adaptation seems too drastic for the desert plant if that adaptation will conserve water. Some plants not only let their leaves die off as the New York apple tree does in winter, they even let whole branches die and fall each year. Nature will do anything to the individual if it helps to keep the species alive.

Every plant, every animal, including man, must maintain its water balance. Each has a certain amount of water in its body. That amount is necessary to keep the plant or animal alive and in good health. Water is necessary to the sap which carries nourishment to roots, stems, branches, leaves, flowers, and fruit. It keeps the cells of living plants in their normal stiff or filled-out condition. Chlorophyll, the green material in plants, uses air, water, and the minerals carried by plant water to make food.

When a plant loses water faster than it is replaced, the cells collapse. The "factory" shuts down. We say the

*These bushes in Rub' al Khali (the Empty Quarter of Saudi Arabia)
battled the harsh environment of the desert and lost.*

ARABIAN AMERICAN OIL COMPANY

plant is wilted. If wilting lasts very long some of the plant cells are badly damaged. The plant dies. If the water loss is replaced quickly enough some plants recover. The cells are filled out. The plant again becomes turgid, or stiff, and upright.

Many botanists say that there are few if any desert plants that can withstand wilting without injury. However, D. N. Kackarov and E. P. Korovini, who worked in the Kara Kum Desert of western Asia, found plants like *Scaligeria, Eremostachys,* and some others that had wilted leaves all day. "The bulbs of these plants," they said, "were incapable of maintaining the plant in water balance."

I have not seen wilted desert plants recover, but I have seen plants in our Wisconsin northwoods recover day after day from midday wilting. Here, at Wisconsin Gardens, we have several stands of jewel weed. On hot days in July and August every summer the jewel weed leaves become limp and droop as if shrinking away from the heat. The flowers, however, remain turgid, always ready to be pollinated. Late in the afternoon, when the swamp begins to cool off, the leaves and wilted small branches regain their turgidity. Our jewel weed tolerates daily wilting for several days at a time but there is always plenty of water from which the roots can replace the loss as soon as the heat crisis is passed.

Those wilted plants reported from the Kara Kum undoubtedly were near a water supply which is regularly replaced. Such replacement is at a very slow rate, too slow, apparently, for the roots to keep the plants turgid through the hot hours of midday. Water resources of that character are not very common in deserts. That may be why wilting plants are encountered only rarely by desert botanists.

All over the world green plants lose their leaves and shut down their food factories when water is in short supply for any reason. The apple tree cuts down evaporation by dropping its leaves before the ground around its gathering field freezes. The desert quickies not only lose their leaves, but the whole plant dies, and survival for the species is through the seeds only. Some desert perennials let their leaves drop off at the beginning of summer, when water becomes scarce, just as the apple trees do at the approach of winter. In both cases the loss of leaves reduces water loss from evaporation.

In Khartoum, Sudan, the semi-desert landscape is a barren plain before the rains come. A few leafless bushes and dead plant stubs or dried grass make it look as lifeless as any desert. During the rainy season, however, those seemingly dead bushes become dense-leafed *Acacia nubica.* The dry stubs change to bunches of grass that make a horizon-to-horizon green carpet. Other acacias, *A. tortilis* and *A. raddiana,* do not shed all their leaves at once. Throughout the dry season they keep losing enough leaves to keep the plant in water balance as the dryness increases.

Some plants found all the way from the Sahara to Mongolia are known as aphyllous plants. Aphyllous means leafless, and this group has such inconspicuous leaves, if they have any at all, that they look like switches.

The switch plants include *Calligonum comosum.* This species has short, threadlike leaves but they are quickly shed when drought begins.

Some plants shed their leaves in summer but the leaf stem stays green. It continues the food-making process. Other plants have large winter leaves at their base. When spring comes the winter leaves dry up. Small leaves come out on the flower stalk and keep producing food all summer. They keep the plant alive, but they are so small that very little water is wasted by evaporation.

The creosote bush, *Larrea divaricata,* covers about thirty-five million acres in the deserts of the American Southwest. It is one of the best equipped plants for desert survival. In addition to the plant's extensive root system, with its keep-your-distance poison to restrict competition, the bush can lose its mature lower leaves in time of drought. The small leaves of the buds stay alive. When moisture is available those brown buds become growing shoots.

A more spectacular leaf-loser is the long-branched candlewood of America's southwest deserts. When in full leaf it requires a lot of water even though the leaves are quite small. At the first sign of drought *Fouquieria splendens* loses all its leaves. Only the bare stem is left exposed to the dry air. The plant quickly responds to moisture however, and the little leaves come out again immediately after a good shower. Candlewood is so sensitive to drought and to moisture changes that it may produce half a dozen crops of leaves in one year, if there are enough good showers. So important is even a little water that you may see a leafless plant only a few yards from one in full leaf. That shows how erratic and limited desert showers can be. When there is a long-lasting water supply the plant will keep its tiny leaves for months. Certainly it is one of the best adapted to unpredictable desert conditions.

Candlewood gets its name from the cluster of scarlet flowers on the tip of each branch. When in blossom, the plants look like flaming torches. The wood of the stem is rich in resin and burns with a steady, blue flame, but the name refers to the red flowers.

An extreme contrast to the tiny, oft-falling leaves of the candlewood are the two leaves of *Welwitchia bainesi* (called *mirabilis* by its discoverer). This strange plant grows in the Namib Desert of southwest Africa. It has a short taproot when it grows in flat depressions in a plain. The trunk or stem is only a few inches high. The stem stops growing upward almost as soon as two lily-like leaves appear. Those two leaves last the lifetime of the plant. Some botanists believe that may be a thousand years! The two leaves continue to grow at the base, and split so that they appear to be several leaves around the central stem. Eventually the plant looks like a large, round coffee table. It never has more than the original two leaves, no matter how often they have split.

In the Namib Desert, where this weird plant grows, it may not rain for ten years. Very often, however, cold night fog rolls in from the sea. The long, narrow leaves, snaking across the desert, cool faster than the air around them. Fog condenses on the leaves. The water runs down to the ground, where the roots can pick it up. Probably the taproot also reaches damp earth, but certainly condensation helps the plant to survive.

Other desert plants, especially those growing within a few miles of the seashore, make use of air moisture. Those with long, narrow leaves, especially grasses, are able to cool down their leaves better than the others. When the leaves are cooled below the dew point, air moisture is condensed. There is some evidence that such moisture is absorbed into the leaves to supplement the plant's root water. At any rate, evaporation of the dew helps to keep a plant cool when heat begins to rise on the desert. Anything which slows loss of moisture from a plant's sap gives that plant a little advantage for survival.

Besides falling off when drought begins, there are many tricks leaves can use to prevent waste of moisture. *Fredolia aretiodes* which grows in the North African Sahara and the eucalyptus have their leaves turned or twisted. Only the edge is toward the sun during the heat of the day. This is a trick also used by the leatherleaf (*Chamaedaphne calyculata,* part of the heath family), which grows in our sphagnum swamp at Wisconsin Gardens. I've seen those straight-up leaves all over the swamp so often that I supposed they always grew that way. Not so, however. The other day I found a patch of plants shaded by some black spruce trees. All the plant leaves stood out at right angles to the stems. Apparently they needed all the light they could get, in contrast to plants in the open, which, like desert plants, need to cut down their water loss.

The leaves of the guayule, a rubber plant of the American deserts, and those of the brittlebush carry on chemical warfare against the seedlings of other plants. Under each of those plants there are big holes in the new spring carpet of desert wild flowers. Their leaves produce a poison, 3-acetyl-6-methoxy benzaldehyde, that kills off all seedlings except those of their own species. There is one other exception: they also tolerate the young sunflower plants. The cleared space in the solid flower carpet insure brittlebush and guayule of the water their roots will need to keep the plants in good health.

Some desert plants roll up or curl their leaves at midday. That way they present the minimum surface to the dry air. The leaves unroll in the cool of late afternoon. Other plants have heavy stems and leaves that keep part of the plant always in the shade as the sun swings from east to west.

All plants must breathe. They take in carbon dioxide from the air and give out oxygen. The pores, through which that exchange takes place, can also let out moisture. Some desert plants, *Altriplex cana* for example, have these pores or stomata on the underside of the leaf. It is cooler there, so less moisture is pulled out. In some cases there are valves that can close against the heat when necessary and still further reduce the loss. A few experiments seem to show that very little moisture is conserved in this way. But one must remember that in the desert there is a very thin margin of safety. Even a tiny saving can mean survival in that harsh climate.

A few plants, like the creosote bush, have a waxy leaf

with a shiny, varnish-like surface. It reflects both heat and light. Of course, the best example of wax coating to prevent loss of moisture is candelilla. *Pedilanthus pavonis* and *Euphorbia cerifera* are two species found in American deserts in the area of Big Bend National Park. They are also found in Mexico, New Mexico, Arizona, and California. The plants are reed-like stems two to four feet high but only one-quarter to one-half inch in diameter. These slender reeds are so coated with wax that it amounts to from 2.25 to 5 percent of the plant's dry weight.

Candelilla wax has a very high melting point (nearly 150° F) and takes a high polish. It has many commercial uses, from shoe polish to electric insulators. The plant is harvested in Mexico under a government monopoly, and the crude wax is shipped across the border to be refined. Several million dollars worth of candelilla wax is produced every year.

The smoke tree and crucifixion thorn of the American Southwest have almost no leaves. Their green stems and thorns carry on the food-making job in place of leaves. Other plants in the deserts of America, Africa, and Asia have many thorns. Some botanists believe that the thorns protect the plant against being eaten by browsing animals. Perhaps they are right. In each of those deserts there are many animals which are heavy browsers. Certainly the thorns don't bother the camels, but they are not wild animals. Australian deserts do not have many thorn-covered plants. Neither are there many native browsing creatures which might eat such plants. Whether or not thorns do protect the plants against being eaten, they can do the work of leaves without wasting so much water.

If you are walking across the desert and see whole branches of a large plant lying dead and broken, you might assume that the plant is dying. If it happens to be *Calligonum comosum*, you've guessed wrong. That plant is just cutting down its evaporation surface for the dry season. Branch shedding looks more dramatic than leaf shedding, but it serves the same purpose. When the rain comes and the desert is again favorable, *Calligonum comosum* will continue to grow as well as ever.

Anabasis articulata doesn't drop its branches. Instead, the green outer bark of last season's growth splits and falls away. Any green part of the plant can carry on photosynthesis, and it also evaporates moisture. Desert plants seem to have adopted every conceivable water-saving device to keep a water balance. To paraphrase Rudyard Kipling, there are nine and sixty ways of meeting desert days and every single one of them is right.

7

Weird and Fantastic

Chapter 6 explained most of the water conservation tricks used by desert plants to survive. Those plants are amateurs compared to the succulents of this chapter and the cactuses described in Chapter 8.

You'll find the baobab trees across Africa from Senegal to Tanganyika. You'll find them in the "land of thirst" on Madagascar and in India. *Pachypodium,* thick-footed ones, the botanists call them. There are five different species of *Pachypodium* in South Africa. They like it on the wet side of the ten-inch isoyette (rainfall line). That seems to put them off limits for this book by most desert definitions. However, in that part of Africa evaporation is so high that desert or semi-desert conditions are characteristic even of twenty-inch-rainfall plains.

The baobab "looks like a carrot planted upside down," said David Livingstone, the early explorer who wandered about Africa as a medical missionary. Even the wild bushmen claim that "when trees were given out the hyena got the last one. He was so mad that he planted it upside down for spite."

A more poetic observer said, "The baobab looks like a tree growing out of a Grecian urn." Most observers seem to prefer terms like bloated bottle, grotesque, unnatural, unwieldly. Some natives call it "the good-for-nothing tree." But in one clan of the Twamumba tribe prayers are offered to the baobab. The clan members claim that their ancestors lived in it exclusively.

Some species are large, "like a silo with branches," 75 feet in circumference for the first 60 feet of height. One is a short shrub which looks much like a large stone with straight handles. Elizabeth Marshall Thomas tells of a tree she calls the Gautscha baobab which she climbed part of the way on pegs. It is 20 feet in diameter, over 60 feet around, and nearly 200 feet high. Its first branches are only 15 feet up. Other baobabs have been reported with circumferences of 130 feet.

Occasionally natives have made their cave home in the hollow of a living baobab. There is a bus stop in one such tree which can shelter 30 people. In another town there is a live baobab that houses a bar with several stools. If you want to make a mummy of a dead animal, just hang it in a hollow baobab. There, protected from outside weather changes, it will desiccate without spoiling.

This weird monarch of the vegetable kingdom is a succulent, a thick plant full of juice. All succulents store moisture for use in long dry periods. In the baobabs the storage is in the spongy trunk and swollen branches. There are few true leaves except in clusters at the top of the tree and at the ends of the branches. There are spine-like spicules or tiny leaves along the branches of

A baobab tree in East Africa.

some species. Others have spines instead of leaves.

The bark is often pinkish-gray and resembles an elephant's hide. Many trees have smooth bark but in some the bark is wrinkled or folded. In the Cameroons people make waterproof hats, drinking cups, and beer steins of baobab bark. Waterproof bark is as characteristic of succulent plants as their capacity for water storage.

A baobab tree usually stands alone, a rugged individualist, a sentinel standing out on the arid plain. When one learns that its roots sometimes go out a hundred yards from the trunk to collect moisture in the rainy season, its isolation is explained. That combination of large gathering field and water-storage capacity is excellent for survival in the land of thirst.

No one knows how old the largest trees may be, because there are no annual rings of growth. One early botanist thought they probably rivaled the redwoods as the oldest living plants on earth. More recent scientists simply say, they don't know.

Young baobabs are tall and slender. No one would take them for the offspring of the fat-trunked adults, except that young leaves look like those of old trees. When old age and death finally catch up with the baobab it doesn't rot slowly like a sturdy oak or a majestic pine tree. Instead, it disintegrates into a pile of dust and blows away on the wind.

Another grotesque-looking succulent is the Joshua tree of Arizona, Utah, and California. Don't confuse it with a cactus. Its specific name is *Yucca brevifolia*. Like Spanish bayonette and other yuccas, the Joshua tree belongs to the lily family. It doesn't look like its relatives, lily-of-the-valley, grape hyacinth, and a host of other familiar flowers. Nevertheless, botanists find the relationship by close study of the leaves and flowers. The thick evergreen leaves and green, soft, porous trunk can hold a lot of water. A wax coating protects it against evaporation in the dry air.

Joshua trees resist scorching summer heat and winter cold. They grow in the desert above a 2,500-foot altitude, and their good health seems to depend on the rest that a cold winter gives them.

In its early youth, the tree is a straight trunk with a topknot of green, dagger-pointed leaves. Old leaves hang on after new ones grow out. Soon they come so far down the trunk that the tree looks like the brush of a fox pointing up in the air. The Joshua doesn't start to branch out until it is eight feet tall, maybe not until it reaches fifteen feet. When it finally does branch out it grows at all sorts of crazy angles—right, left, south, north, up, and even down. It has no twigs, only branches, each with a cluster of thick-bodied, sharp-pointed leaves at the end. Old leaves hanging on make the whole tree look shaggy.

Old Joshua trees are so grotesque that they make one think of many-limbed, prehistoric monsters. But every spring flower buds appear at the end of each branch. At first each bud resembles an artichoke. Then the bud begins to open. Ivory-white flowers push out into beautiful clusters. A Joshua tree in the moonlight then has a strange beauty added to its grotesque silhouette. Beautiful or grotesque as it may be, the Joshua Tree can meet the des-

Young Joshua trees grow straight up for eight to fifteen feet before they start to branch.

Mature Joshua tree. This yucca, which is related to the Spanish bayonette and other members of the lily family, dominates the landscape at Joshua Tree National Monument.

ert contrasts of heat, cold, long dry spells, or short moisture periods and still produce blossoms year after year. I
wonder how the Mormons associated *Yucca brevifolia*,
whose "arms" point in all directions, with Joshua, who
pointed to the Promised Land?

American succulents include the agaves, which have
a rosette of fleshy, fibrous leaves, saw-tooth-edged and
spine-pointed. Like other succulents, the agaves are
found in two-rainy-season deserts. Although they tolerate long dry spells the succulents need moisture replacement, even though it be scanty, during the summer and
again in the winter. That is why there are no succulents
in the deep Sahara and other single-season-moisture deserts. The fibrous leaves store water to keep the plant in
water balance when the soil is dry. Their murderous
edges and spear-sharp points keep many animals from
eating these juicy morsels.

The best known of the group is the *Agave americana*,
the century plant. True, it takes years to produce its
blossoms, but not a hundred years, as its name implies.
When the plant reaches maturity all its energy is concentrated to produce the flowers and seeds. In a few days
the bud of the flower stalk grows to eighteen or twenty
feet in height. It tops out in a flower cluster of seven
thousand blossoms. After the seeds are ripe the plant dies.

Several species of agave are grown commercially for
their fiber. In fact, the sisal industries of India and Africa
were made possible when the agave plants were introduced there from America.

Agave palmeri and two or three other species are

A century plant, Agave americana, *in bloom in Big Bend National Park.*

BIG BEND NATIONAL PARK

grown in fields in Mexico. They are the basis for popular Mexican drinks called mezcal and tequila. When the plants are eight to ten years old and the flower-stalk bud is ready to expand, the short trunk is rich in sugars. That is when the harvest begins. The thick, juicy leaves are cut away. The thick, short trunk is roasted to free some of the sugars. Then the roasted trunk is allowed to ferment and convert the sugars to alcohol. The alcohol is recovered by distilling the mass.

If the price of sisal is high enough the discarded leaves are marketed for their fiber. Generally they are not worth the extra labor because several species are grown in the same field and mixed fibers do not bring quality prices.

A group of succulents native to southwest Africa has evolved a very complicated way of meeting the survival problems. They are called flowering stones and window plants. The first one was discovered about 1811 by the British traveler William John Burchell. His book, *Travels in the Interior of Southern Africa,* was published in London in 1822–24.

While out on the Karroo Plateau, northeast of Cape Town, Burchell stooped down to pick up an oddly shaped pebble. Instead of a stone he found he had a living plant. Later, his drawings were lost, and no one else could find the plant even though they hunted on the same stony plain. Finally, in 1918, more than 100 years after Burchell's discovery, Dr. J. B. Pole-Evans of Pretoria rediscovered it. A botanist, Dr. N. E. Brown, named the plant *Lithops turbiformes*. The Hottentots in the area called it sheep's hoof.

These interesting plants are so close to the ground and unprotected that they probably endure more severe desert conditions than any other adult flowering plants. Where they grow, the plant body catches the full force of desert heat. Down close to the ground the combination of direct sun and reflected heat produces summer temperature as high as 133° F. That is much higher than official free-air temperature, which must be taken five feet above ground in a ventilated shelter. In winter the leaves are surrounded by air at 14° F. Besides high temperatures and chilling cold, the plants are exposed to the full force of sunlight, more than can be used for photosynthesis. Some of them live and prosper in the Namib Desert, where there is seldom more than half an inch of rain per year, although sea fogs keep the air more humid than that of some ten-inch-rainfall deserts. Survival for the stone plants presents more problems than are encountered by most desert vegetation. But they do survive, proving that no matter how tough the problem of survival, nature has solved it somehow, somewhere, sometime.

The window plant (*Lithops turbiniformis*) has two leaves touching each other on a very short, round stem. The leaves are thick and make an upside-down cone. Its broad base is up above ground. Its pointed end is buried. The green chlorophyll is on the inside of the tissue that forms the outside of the buried cone.

Chlorophyll must have sunlight. It is the energy necessary to produce plant food. How can sunlight reach the buried chlorophyll? It passes through the window-like tops of the leaves which are above ground. Some win-

Stone plants in bloom.

dow plants have tiny, transparent "panes" separated by opaque dividers. Whether the windows are large or small they let through enough light for the food factory to operate.

Stone plants come by their name honestly. During the dry season many of them are completely dormant. They blend perfectly with the stony desert floor on which they live. One group, the genus *Gobbaeum* (it means hump) is silver-colored and blends with the white quartz around it. *Pleiospilos bolusii* looks like dried liver, but it also resembles the chunks of iron ore that weather out from the soil around it. Another species is so camouflaged that it is hard to see among the broken pieces of brown slate and sandstone covering the ground where it grows. Still another plant has white, wart-like excrescences on the leaves. Those leaves can hardly be distinguished from the surrounding weathered limestone.

Naturally one wonders why such protective coloring is necessary. Some observers have suggested that it is to protect the plant from being eaten by antelope, which range the desert. Biologists, however, believe that antelope are guided to their food by the sense of smell rather than that of sight. Perhaps during the time the stone plants evolved some other food-searcher needed to be fooled. At any rate, protective coloring and simulation of its surroundings protected the stone plant from modern man for over a hundred years.

Desert adaptation of *Lithops* doesn't stop with its sunlight filters and imitations of its surroundings. These succulents contain considerable moisture and successfully resist water loss. One *Lithops ruschiorum* plant weighed 11.5 grams (less than half an ounce) when it was exposed to full sunlight for fifteen days. It lost only 0.2 grams, 0-017 of its weight. In their natural surroundings these plants sometimes go a year without rain and still survive.

The blossoms of stone flowers are not very numerous but they are highly scented and easy to see. Honeybees, night-flying insects, and small hover flies cross-pollinate the flowers. The seed capsules and seeds are also adapted for survival in the land of sun and uncertain rain. There are several chambers in the capsule. Each has a lid with a mechanism sensitive to moisture and dryness. When the seeds are ripe the lid remains closed until there is a shower. Rain opens the lid. The seeds are washed out, but as soon as the capsule dries the lid closes. Seeds have remained dry for as long as fourteen years. Even after being dry and dormant for such a long time they were still alive and able to sprout.

Surely these strange plants of southwest Africa have developed most of the "tricks of the trade" for survival in sun and drought. They are far less numerous, however, than the cactuses, those made-in-America plants that have traveled so widely since Columbus discovered the land of their birth.

8

Cactuses — Gypsies and Stay-at-Homes

Cactuses (cacti, if you prefer) are as made-in-America as maize or Indian corn. Although they are native to America, evolved in America, and are most numerous in America, cactus plants are often used as the symbol for deserts throughout the world. Except for two species which reached southern Africa, cactuses were unknown outside America until Columbus found them and took some back to Europe. Today some cactuses are found in Africa, Asia, Australia, southern Europe, and the Near East. Along the northern edge of the Sahara several species of *Opuntia,* the prickly pears, have taken over large areas of land. Berber and Arab peoples make well-worn paths through the spiny jungles while they gather and eat the juicy fruit. Sometimes you can buy fresh cactus fruit in marketplaces. Cactus fruit makes good candy, syrup, and fruit butter.

The genus *Opuntia* are the real gypsies of the cactus group. I have found tiny, dwarf plants growing in a spoonful of soil on otherwise bare rock at Interstate Park, Wisconsin. That is a thousand miles north of their normal arid-zone habitat. The bare rock at Interstate probably gets as hot in summer as it ever does in the southwest desert but it also gets down to 50° below zero, Fahrenheit in winter. I never found one of the Wisconsin plants in blossom and I have no idea how the seeds reached the barren, glaciated rock, but the plants survive both heat and cold. Plants of the genus *Opuntia* are good travelers. They find their place in the sun anywhere in the world if there are a few heavy rains once a year.

The spine-covered green paddles of prickly pear plants are not leaves, even though they look like them. These thick, rounded segments are joints of the stem. Some species do have a few small leaves when the plants are young. They also appear on joints of new growth, but they are shed early. Photosynthesis is carried on by the stem itself and by the spines which cover its flat surfaces. The thick joints also store water which the network of shallow roots collects during the rainy season.

At about the end of the rainy season large, colorful flowers open out along the edge of the upper joints. After they are pollinated the fruit begins to swell and the paddles are edged with rows of large, green warts. These, too, are covered with spines, but they are not as murderous as the hard spines of the joints.

Even on dead joints the spines are wicked weapons of defense. Natives in the northern Sahara plant the joints along the tops of their garden walls. Occasionally they take root in the dry adobe, but whether they grow or not they are as good a defense against wall-climbing trespassers as a topping of pieces of broken glass.

Prickly pear. The spine-shadow pattern changes constantly as the sun moves west and helps to cool the plant. Note the fuzzy-cushioned pockets from which the spines grow. The cushions help prevent evaporation of moisture from inside the plant and also keep out the heat.

MERVIN W. LARSON, ARIZONA-SONORA DESERT MUSEUM

When the thorns are removed prickly pear makes good cattle food. During severe drought in the Southwest, when nothing else is available and cattle are starving, the cattlemen burn off the needles. In addition to moisture, the plants have a good percentage of food protein. Burning off the needles with a blowtorch requires too much labor to justify using the plant except in emergencies.

The species *Opuntia cochinillifera* is the host for a tiny insect, *Dactylopius coccus,* from which cochineal, a brilliant scarlet dye, is made. Indians were producing it for trade with other Indians in 1518, when Spain conquered Mexico. The Spaniards carried the industry to Spain. It also reached India, Algiers, South Africa, Jamaica, and the Canary Islands. That *Opuntia* was a real gypsy, you see. It wasn't until 1703, however, that scientific use of a microscope proved that the "grains" which were brushed off the plant were insects. They can be "planted" on cactus joints and will multiply there rapidly. In four months they are numerous enough to be dusted off into baskets and dried. Two or three harvests a year are possible.

There is a legend about the *Opuntia.* I find it interesting because it illustrates several desert-survival characteristics.

Long, long ago the rain-god was giving the earth a good soaking. Then the wind-god thought it would be fun to frustrate his friend. He puffed a big wind that blew the rain into a great black cloud and dried up the falling water before it could reach the thirsty earth.

Rain-god couldn't see anything funny in that practical

joke. He sulked in his castle and refused to give the earth any more rain. The soil dried. Plants began to wilt. Flowers dried before they could set seeds. Plant and seed-eating animals, big and little, lost weight and began to die of dehydration. The drought became a crisis. Before it got to be a catastrophe the wind-god sent his daughter as "a committee of one" to plead with the rain-god.

That lovely girl started west. The wind-god tried to keep her comfortable with a gentle breeze, but even the lightest wind evaporated more and more moisture from her body. Dehydration began to dull her senses. She could see nothing ahead but blurred sand underfoot. There seemed to be a fuzzy haze in the air and blurry, spine-covered *Opuntias* all around her. Half blind and thoroughly confused she struggled on, but her steps faltered. The brassy light of midday hurt her eyes. Her sight blurred. At two o'clock she collapsed, exhausted and weak from heat and dehydration.

Fortunately she fell in the shade of a large, many-branched *Opuntia*. There it was 30 degrees cooler than in the sun where she had been trying to walk. She slept. The brassy sun moved over the horizon. The drying wind ceased. In the cool of early evening the girl woke. Above her head she saw a single fruit on the edge of the cactus. She plucked it, rubbed off the prickles, and ate the juicy fruit. Even that little moisture, added to her afternoon nap, revived her dehydrated body. She continued her westward journey.

Opuntias lined her route so that she could not stray out into the desert. The plants forced her to walk in a straight line. Every few steps she plucked another fruit to eat. Each mouthful of the juicy pulp seemed to restore her strength. When the brilliant moonlight flooded the desert and cast blue-black shadows ahead, she came out of the spiny jungle. There was a beautiful waterfall, the dream of every lost desert traveler.

This, of course, was no dream. It was a real waterfall and the rain-god's castle stood high on the cliff beside it. Naturally the legend ends as all good legends should. The rain-god spotted the lovely desert wanderer. He found her pleasant to look at and agreed to her plea. He stopped sulking and sent rain to the parched earth.

Rain-god, and wind-god and his daughter, agreed, however, that a large section of the earth should be set aside for the cactus. Only enough water should fall there to keep the cactus healthy. After all, it was the cactus that had sheltered the lovely girl. It had revived her with its moisture-filled fruit and guided her to the rain-god's castle.

The barrel cactus, bisnaga, is equipped for survival in even drier deserts than opuntia can tolerate. These plants also have a good record for providing survival water to desert travelers lost in the wilderness. Their shallow roots make an efficient gathering field when a light shower dampens their area. They often extend to a distance that is twelve times the height of the plant, but they reach only three or four inches below the desert surface. Such roots are a poor anchor when heavy rains soften the ground around them. The plants may topple over from their own weight after unusually heavy rains, but that

is a minor hazard, for the roots continue to gather moisture and the prostrate bisnaga survives in the new
position.

The pulpy interior of the plant absorbs and holds
moisture like a sponge. The hard, spine-covered shell protects it against evaporation. Even months after a rain, the
bisnaga is so full of juice that you can get a good drink
by squeezing a chunk of pulp into your mouth.

The barrel shape is, next to a true sphere, the most
economical wall form for surrounding any mass. In the
bisnaga that shape protects the greatest mass of moisture-holding pulp with the minimum surface exposed to
air and sun. A two-hundred-pound plant may have only
ten square feet of surface. One species in Central America grows six to nine feet tall and three to four feet in
diameter. Such a plant may weigh two tons.

The efficiency of its shape is increased by "accordion
pleats" in the outer shell. When moisture is plentiful the
plant swells. The spine-covered ridges become farther
apart and the valleys become smooth plains. When
drought increases, the outer shell shrinks. The ridges
come closer together and the rows of defensive spines
close ranks to make it difficult for any browsing animal
to get at the stored moisture.

I've heard many arguments against the use of cactus
juice as a desert survival drink. Such arguments are generally given by armchair travelers. Practical field workers
and at least one tough Marine Corps lieutenant have
given us first-hand reports. Those leave no doubt that
the juice of the bisnaga is potable and is a lifesaver for

the desert for five days before he was spotted from a
　First Lieutenant Edwin Wladislaus Zolnier parachuted
from his burning plane while flying over the desert. He
landed safely far out on the desert. In the wide-open
spaces of the Arizona desert there are no handy telephones
to use in such an emergency. A man alone is hard to find
amid the rocks and desert plants, even when searchers
have a general idea of where to look. Lt. Zolnier walked
the desert traveler whose gallon canteen has gone dry.
search plane and a ground rescue party was guided to
him.

　"I wouldn't be here today," he said in a letter to
Ladislaus Clark, author of an article in the *Missouri Botanical Garden Bulletin,* "if it weren't for the barrel cactus."

　Lt. Zolnier tried the moisture of a thirty-foot-high
cactus when he first got thirsty but "found it very nau-
seating." Later he found a barrel cactus "and chewed
the water out of large chunks cut from the living plant."
It tasted pleasant at first but eventually became monotonous. The marine hacked open barrel cacti whenever he
found them during his walk. He sucked out the juice for
drinking, carried large chunks in his clothing, and even
rubbed his body with them. The moisture, of course,
cooled his body just as perspiration does and so conserved
his own body moisture.

　Mr. Clark also tells of tasting several species of barrel
cactus in different parts of the southwest. He tried them
out on friends at a dinner party. Everyone found the
juice potable and none found it unpleasant or nauseat-

The Barrel cactus is the drinking fountain for lost travelers in American deserts. The thick lattice-work of spines keeps the plant in cool shade despite intense sun, while photosynthesis is carried on by the spines to produce food.

MERVIN W. LARSON, ARIZONA-SONORA DESERT MUSEUM

ing. People's tastes, however, differ widely.

"Cool and pleasant," one called it. "A delicate flavor of coconut," said another. "Monotonous as distilled water"; "slightly salty if you get a large enough quantity at a time" are other comments. Mr. Randall Henderson, formerly the editor of *Desert Magazine,* thought it tasted a little like the aftertaste of an aspirin tablet.

No one seems to have had difficulty getting at the juice of the barrel cactus even when they forgot their hatchet or machete. One person just gave a plant a swift kick and it toppled over. Then he broke it open with a stone.

At least it is certain that the bisnaga has met the survival problem of holding moisture from rain. That is how it can regularly produce flowers for reproduction and incidentally serve as an emergency drinking fountain for the thirsty traveler. It is also something of a "compass plant."

If you look closely at a number of the plants you may discover a tendency for them to lean in one direction more than any other. That favored direction is generally southwest. Be sure that your statistics are based on a large enough numerical sample. As with all "compass plants," it is necessary to observe the average direction indicated by many plants. Never, but *never,* rely on one or two.

The real stay-at-home is the saguaro, or giant cactus. It was once called *Carnegiea gigantea* but now botanists call it *Cereus giganteus.* Its range is limited to Arizona, southeastern California, and Sonora, Mexico. Wherever it grows it dominates the scenery like a true giant. Car-

toonists who want to indicate a desert often place a lone-
some saguaro on a featureless plain—where it never grows.
The giant does well in the midst of cat-claw, mesquite,
and palo-verde, and with smaller cactuses on rough or
rocky terrain.

Cereus giganteus may grow two feet in diameter and
forty to fifty feet tall. But it is a slow grower. A ten-year
old is seldom more than five inches high, but in the course
of two hundred years it encounters enough good growing
seasons to make it a real giant.

The ability to hold water against evaporation is, perhaps, its most spectacular survival adaptation. Someone
has estimated the capacity for a big plant to be six to
eight *tons*. Only a thimbleful of moisture per day is lost by
evaporation. No wonder the desert giant can flower and
ripen fruit every year on schedule, whether or not it
rains.

The young saguaro is a round, fluted stem growing
straight up like a telephone pole. The ridges of its fluting
have a line of spines like those of other cacti. A tube
made up of woody ribs is buried in the moisture-holding
pulp. It protects the heart of the plant and also gives
the plant a strong support against the desert winds. The
ribs are strong rods which taper like a fishpole. The
Papago Indians used them as part of house roofs. They
also served to make cradleboard frames for the babies
and as carrying poles for heavy loads.

In the course of several decades a sturdy saguaro may
get injured in such a way that a branch starts off at
right angles to the main stem. Perhaps an unusual grow-

ing season also stimulates expansion. At any rate, older plants have one or more branches which turn up close to the trunk and grow parallel to the main stem. Each holds its crown of annual blossoms upright to the sun.

The giant is no selfish bully, even if it is armed with a tough hide and spear-sharp spines. In dry years, when other succulent food is hard to find, rodents feed on the giant's body as far as they can get among the spines. Gila woodpeckers drill nesting holes high up in the trunk valleys between the spine-covered ridges. They drill through the tough, waterproof hide into the juicy pulp but never cut deeper than the rib cage which protects the giant's heart. Those holes don't bother the saguaro at all if they are made in the dry season. The plant just lines the injury with fiber which soon gets as hard as a pine knot. It makes a cool nest for the young woodpeckers and eventually serves the Indians as a solid, waterproof container. When the woodpecker abandons the pocket a new tenant, the pygmy owl, moves in. Mary Austin, who loved the Southwest and published several books about it, once saw a saguaro with "seventeen woodpecker holes like the little openings of the old cliffdweller caves."

Little blue-headed hawks use the giant as a lookout tower to spot their prey on the desert floor. In the crotch of an ancient saguaro, the red-tailed hawk builds its nest. While that family stays at home there will be neither bird nor rodent at the giant's feet. The redtails guarantee to prevent a population explosion among their neighbors and to maintain a nice balance between food supply and desert population.

Saguaro, Cereus giganteus, *is the real giant of the cactuses. Note the rows of spines on the barrel cactuses (lower right), which twist toward the southwest.*

SAGUARO NATIONAL MONUMENT

In a survival contest for plants of the desert world cactuses would win the blue ribbon. They have managed to survive in a changing world for fifty million years. Ever since the Eocene epoch, when their ancestors grew on the seashore in the humid climate, cactuses have successfully adapted to changes and a drying environment.

Botanists can trace some of those adaptations in species still found in parts of America. One of the *Pereskia,* a cactus with leaves and spines at the base of each leaf petiole, still grows in the jungles of the West Indies. That species is unchanged from its Eocene ancestors. *Pereskia guamacho,* native to the Orinoco basin in Venezuela, has leaves that possess some medicinal value. The wood of the plant is not strong but when it is used for fenceposts it keeps on growing, making a formidable hedge with its spine-based leaves.

At the other end of the evolutionary series are the pincushion cactus and the giant saguaro. The pincushion is a spine-covered, one-inch ball found on the floor of the Grand Canyon in Arizona. The saguaro, the fifty-foot, six-ton giant, grows on the plateau up to 3,500 feet above sea level. Both have given up leaves entirely and replaced them with evaporation-resisting spines.

Between the leafy, wet-jungle species and the all-spine, dry-desert group is the *Opuntia.* On new joints of the *Opuntia* small, thick ephemeral leaves appear. Their temporary presence testifies to the plant's origin, but they don't last long. Spines and thick, green stem joints which look like leaves do the work performed by leaves in more humid regions.

Opuntia is the great survivor now. Man has made its travels easy and most of its species have been generally welcome because of the appetizing fruit. Not in New South Wales and Queensland, Australia, however! There *Opuntia vulgaris balearica* has become a pest. It has run wild over thousands of acres of good agricultural land. It spread so fast that its adaptability has been called one of the wonders of the plant world. Not until an insect enemy was also introduced could the spread of this "survival expert" be controlled. Astronauts had better be careful not to have any *Opuntia* seeds caught in their clothing when they go to the moon. Any plant that has been so successful at meeting environmental changes for fifty million years might take over the lunar landscape if given half a chance.

Although all cactuses are succulents, not all succulents are cactuses. That should not confuse you in identifying a cactus, because cactuses have five distinct characteristics.

1. All have areoles, small pits on the stem where the axils of leaves would be and from which the spines and the flowers grow. If all the areoles are removed the plant will die. These little openings have fuzzy centers that act as insulation to keep heat out of the plant and hold moisture in.

2. All cactuses are perennial. They take more than one year to reach maturity.

3. They have wheel- or funnel-shaped flowers. The sepals and petals grow from the wide part of an inverted bell-shaped tube. The seeds develop in the narrow part

of the tube below the flower.

4. Seeds are scattered through the fruit pulp as in a watermelon, not in separate cells as in an apple or an orange.

5. The seed sprouts into two embryo leaves which are lost very soon after sprouting.

Botanists have described 1,752 species of cactuses. All but two, which are native to South Africa, belong to America. Perhaps those two African species got carried over there by birds long, long ago. At least 60 species are found in Arizona. The plants are so typical of the state that the saguaro is the state flower.

As a group the cactuses cover the whole range of water-conserving adaptations. Extensive, shallow root systems collect water from a desert shower before much of it is evaporated. Thick, pulpy stems absorb water like a sponge and their tough, wax-coated outer covering protects the stored moisture from evaporation. You can see how effective that outer skin is by peeling half of a prickly-pear paddle. The skinned half will dry and shrivel in a few hours, while the covered section retains its moisture.

Green spines and green stems instead of leaves manufacture food for the plant. The spines are protection against browsing animals. They do serve that function to a certain extent, although starving cattle will eat the succulent cactus joints despite the thorns. When they are hungry enough they have been seen with their faces bristling with cactus thorns.

Spines also have a more important function. They form

a lattice shade for the plant. Like the round shape of the stems, they keep the body of the plant constantly in partial shade. As the sun swings through its arch from sunrise to sunset the plant is at least 20° cooler in the shaded parts than it would be without its private air conditioning system. In short, every inch of a cactus constantly contributes to its system of water conservation. That is why cactuses flower on schedule year after year despite unpredictable gaps in the rainfall.

9

The Scarcity of Abundant Life

On the floor of Death Valley, the hot, dry, below-sea-level desert of California, 26 species of mammals have been identified. One observer in the Sahara listed 207 species of birds. Bob Matthews, naturalist for Aramco (Arabian American Oil Company), identified 140 species of birds in Arabia, and Donald A. Holm photographed more than 40 of them in color. In the deserts of Africa and Australia R. M. Elton ate 43 species of insects. The popular writings of Roy Chapman Andrews mention 35 or 40 common animals and birds encountered frequently in the Gobi. That doesn't include the scores of species listed in the scientific publications of his expeditions. Russian scientists list 40 mammals in the northwest Gobi and 22 kinds of fleas found on the carnivores.

Fish, frogs, tortoises, crocodiles, snakes, bats, vultures, hawks, owls, antelope, rats, foxes, wild asses, wolves, mountain sheep and goats, camels, lizards, ducks, woodpeckers, wrens, and ostriches: the list of identified desert wildlife reads like a roster from the world's zoological gardens.

Roy Chapman Andrews looks down on young birds in a kite's nest in the badlands of the Gobi Desert.

It is true that those species are all present and ac-
counted for—some of the time, in some corners, somewhere in the desert world. But don't expect to see very
many of them during your first thousand miles of desert
travel, even if you travel on foot or camelback. If you
expect to survive on this rich source of protein food
while you travel the desert you'll need more luck per day
than most of us have per year.

One day in the Gobi we were driving along the rim
of a narrow valley. Just after passing a native well I noticed that the valley swarmed with animals. They were
moving slowly down toward the well. Soon I realized
that this was the largest group of animals I had ever seen
anywhere in the world.

"I'd hate to haul water out of the well for that flock of
sheep," I said to the Chinese cook riding with me.

"Not sheep," he said, "antelope."

I turned for a good look at the valley and almost
rammed the car ahead of me. My companion was right.
The valley was filled with antelope!

Roy Andrews, leader of the expedition, halted our
caravan and we all got off the trucks to watch that moving mass of antelope. Someone noted that the valley was
about a quarter of a mile wide and that we had been
following the herd for nearly three miles.

"Must be 25,000 head of antelope in that mass," Roy
said. "Probably nowhere else in the world could you see
so many wild animals at once, unless it would be the
grasslands of Africa." Where they were going, or why,
none of our zoologists would even guess. In over forty

years of desert experience I have neither seen nor heard of a similar mass movement of antelope. There really is a scarcity of abundant life in the desert, despite the long lists of species compiled by desert travelers. If exceptions prove the rule, our one experience emphasizes that truth.

During our first two or three weeks in the Gobi we did not see one antelope. Later we saw them regularly, and we ate antelope meat twice a day. Generally the animals were in small bands of a dozen or so, sometimes three or four times that number. If our cars turned toward them they raced away across the desert almost parallel to our course. Then they'd cut across our route fifty or seventy-five yards ahead of us.

The animals avoid their carnivorous enemies by their ability to get into high speed in a couple of jumps. They can run 45 mph while their worst enemy, the wolf, has a top speed of only about 30 mph. The wolf lives on the edge of rocky or broken country while the antelope are feeding on the smoother plain. If an antelope strays from the herd the wolf tries to head him onto the broken ground. There the antelope can't travel so fast. Speed isn't exclusively a desert technique for survival, but it helps to keep an antelope out of the mouths of hungry desert carnivores.

Never did we find the animals near a water hole. Never have I seen or heard of a Gobi antelope taking a drink. The same is true for the gazelle in the Sahara and in Arabia. All of these related animals eat grass, of course, and get enough moisture from the vegetation to keep them in a state of water balance.

Antelope have adopted other survival techniques to conserve body water and meet desert harshness. Despite their ability to race out of danger quickly, most of their traveling is slow and leisurely. The great herd we saw in the Gobi valley was moving at an easy walk. Slow motion in the desert keeps down the heat load and reduces perspiration. During the heat of midday the animals disappear from open sunlight and rest in the shade. Once I needed a Sahara gazelle for some scientific comparisons. It was in June, and hot for daytime desert work. I found an Arab sheik who had friends in several oases. Every day for a week we drove to a different locality and sent out native hunters. By 10:00 A.M. our station wagon was like an oven. We sought the partial comfort of darkened adobe houses. Even though the reward was adequate, none of our hunters could find a gazelle. Years later I discovered why.

At a little zoo in Libya I noticed that the gazelle regularly rest in the shade during the heat of the day. The shadow of a single palm leaf can hide an adult gazelle. Apparently they had been hiding in the shade during that week in June, just as the sheik and I had been doing while our hunters were out.

In addition to their ability to keep in water balance without drinking, gazelle and antelope have their young in the climatic spring, when vegetation is green and fresh. That makes a good supply of milk for the youngsters. Animals raised in deserts north of the equator adjust their breeding habits in a couple of seasons if they are moved to deserts south of the equator. In their new habitat the young will be born when the grass is fresh and green, even though it is six months later than spring in their original home.

A few kulon, or wild asses, are still found in the far west of the Gobi. I believe the Russians have been doing some experimental breeding with them on large farms. In the wild, their worst enemy is the wolf. They avoid him as the antelope does, with a swift getaway and by staying as far away from enemy territory as they can. That is especially true at foaling time. The young are born far out on the plain. By the time they are a week old they can run 25 mph and dodge like football players. Unlike the gazelle or antelope, the kulon must drink once a day. Russian scientists who have studied them say that the kulon will trot twenty-five or thirty miles every evening to a waterhole and then back to its feeding grounds.

A ten-inch-rainfall desert may have abundant grass, especially if the scanty rain comes fairly often through the year instead of in a single storm. Once while I was in North Africa a friend lent me a very old travel book about the part of Algeria in which I was working. I have forgotten both its title and the author's name, but it was written long before the French ruled Algeria. It told of lion hunting on the north edge of Sahara. Today a lion would starve to death there, because he would find no grass eaters. They disappeared with the grass long ago. Why did the grass go? There is just as much rain there today as there was two hundred or two thousand years ago. But the lion hunters too often set fire to the

*Sheep and goats in the Arabian Desert will live on scanty vege-
tation, but they crop it so close that large flocks soon reduce plant
cover, expose roots to increased drought, and reduce their holding
power against torrential rains.*

ARABIAN AMERICAN OIL COMPANY

grass to flush out the game. Then, in dry years, herdsmen pastured flocks of sheep and goats that were too large. The domestic flocks cropped the grass so close that it has no chance to cover the desert floor as it once did.

When left undisturbed, wild grass eaters don't overgraze their pasture. Predators kill off the weak, sick, or stupid animals. Survivors move to new pastures before they overgraze an area. Poor grass years are followed by a low birth rate among grass eaters. As we have said before, there is no shortage in the desert. There is just enough for survival.

Once I was sitting on an old Indian village site in Monument Valley, Arizona. Len Hargrave of the Northern Arizona Museum was with me. All around us was bare desert.

"Would you believe that this area was once surrounded with marshy meadow?" he asked.

Naturally my answer was a very skeptical, "Oh yeah?"

"Well, we have the diaries of explorers and records of early trappers," he said. "According to those writings this was good beaver country a couple of hundred years ago. The animals dammed the little streams. The beaver ponds stored water between the rains. Indian gardens were productive around the meadows."

"Why is it desert now?" I asked.

"Beaver hats became stylish," said Hargrave. "Trappers met the demands of fashion with beaver pelts. When the typical storms of this region came, the floods washed out the beaver dams just as they always had. But with the beaver colonies shorthanded or gone, the dams were not replaced. Later, floods caused still more damage. In a few short years the good soil was washed down to the San Juan River. The Indians had to find new areas for their gardens."

There is still abundant grass in parts of Africa where the rainfall is scanty. Grass eaters still thrive there as they once did in the African deserts, especially along stream valleys. Most of the grass eaters, like the kulon of the Gobi, must drink water at regular intervals. When open water dries up in desert heat, the native wildlife beats a path farther and farther from its pasture to another waterhole.

I remember going to a prehistoric habitation site near Tebessa, Algeria. My companion, M. Maurice Reygasse, had collected ancient stone tools there several times. We found the place.

"There's the collecting ground, all right," said my friend. "But it's now on the shore of a pond and I never saw water here before." A little later a native shepherd came over the hill to lead his sheep and goats beside the water. Reygasse questioned the man about the waterhole.

"Oh, yes," he said. "It is here every few years. We had a big rain this spring. When it rains we can use this pasture. Then we don't have to go back to a well and draw water for the flock."

If left alone, desert wildlife finds such waterholes. The grass eaters move from one good pasture to another. The carnivores follow them. Of course, the moisture in the flesh and viscera of their prey helps to keep the wolves, foxes, hyenas, owls, and hawks in water balance. Meat

This desert water hole in northern Algeria had been a dry little hollow in the arid plain for many years, but a big spring rain turned it into a convenient watering place for shepherds and their flocks.

AUTHOR'S PHOTO

eaters, however, require more water than vegetable eaters. There is more waste from meat (protein) than in non-protein foods. Such waste must be eliminated through the animals' kidneys, and therefore, requires a lot of water. After a good meal the carnivores rest in the shade. That keeps their body temperature down to normal without wasting water through sweating. They also hide in caves. A few even dig dens below the hot desert floor. Eighteen inches below the desert floor the animal can rest in a cool atmosphere thirty or forty degrees below the temperature of the desert above. Nevertheless, these animals do have to drink frequently. When the water shortage is really severe they move out of the desert. That's the advantage many animals and birds have over plants, which are anchored to the desert floor. The carnivores survive in the desert by taking advantage of favored corners, not by any major specialization.

In many parts of the desert world it takes very little to change a small corner of uninhabitable land to a place of abundant life. One botanist found only thirteen plant species during a month of travel in the Libyan Desert. He contrasted that scarcity with the many dozens of known species from places in American deserts no larger than an ordinary farm, or collected from a single canyon, or small slope of mesquite.

Such abundance in small areas was emphasized when the American Museum of Natural History established a research station at Cave Creek Canyon, near Portal, Arizona. The canyon is located in the Chiricahua Range of mountains, which rises to almost ten thousand feet altitude between the Sonoran Desert on the west and the Chihuahuan Desert on the east. One can drive from the arid habitat of prickly pear and yucca, road runner and gila monster, through that of kit fox and horned toad, into the dry, temperate zone of rabbit bush and piñon pine, then on through the fourth zone of yellow pine and white-tailed deer to that of the cinnamon bear and Engelman spruce. The five life zones can be covered in less than an hour's drive. It is like driving from Mexico to Canada as far as vegetation and animal life zones are concerned. Only the first three life zones are comparable to the arid and semi-arid lands with which this book is concerned.

Cave Creek Canyon is an exception in the desert world, but any break in the desert characteristics, even on a small scale, can account for abundance where you'd expect scarcity. In the semi-desert areas of South Africa the baobab tree makes such a corner of abundance. The elephantine tree provides a bit of shade in the midst of a sunbaked land. The basin formed by the cluster of branches at the top of the trunk often holds water long after rain pools on the ground have dried up. Such a pool is always a possible habitat for many insects. The insects are food for lizards and birds, which in turn, are food for hawks.

The importance of a single baobab is well indicated by Elizabeth Marshall Thomas in *The Harmless People*. She observed a large baobab over a period of several months. It was visited at regular intervals by bushmen in search of wild honey and other food. Bees lived in a hole high up among the branches. There were many other little holes on the great trunk. Sticking out from some of them were wisps of dried grass, a sure sign that some small creature had its nest there. Among the roots and in the forks of branches larger animals made their homes.

On the south side of the tree a mongoose had once lived in a cave among the tree roots. On the north side a python had found a haven. Green-furred squirrels scampered among the lower branches. Several kinds of small birds found shelter for their nests. Higher up was the nest of a pair of gray hawks.

Such abundance of usually non-desert life is far from characteristic of most arid wastelands. But remember that for many months of the year the area around the great tree is desert. The tree is a haven, a corner of the arid plain which provides that little difference in shade and moisture that makes survival possible.

In American deserts the coyote wells provide similar relief for desert inhabitants. The coyote must drink as well as eat. When the rain pools have dried, he hunts out sheltered spots of moisture. The bend of a riverbed where water was deepest during the flood; a pile of flood debris below a falls, wet sand below an undercut bank or rocky ledge: all are good locations for a coyote well. There he digs a shallow basin with his paws as a dog digs to hide a bone. Water seeps into the open cavity and the coyote drinks.

During the daytime these water pools are gathering points for daylight creatures. At night, animals of the darkness come for water. The coyote takes his toll from these and from the early-morning drinkers, but the coyote's well provides survival water for many more creatures than his hungry stomach demands.

The water level lowers day by day, and day by day the coyote deepens the well to maintain a supply of drinking water. He may even extend the pit to a slanting tunnel several feet long in order to keep the well bottom in the lowering water level. Desert snakes and animals, birds and bees, other insects and lizards all find their way to coyote wells or other waterholes.

In the Namib Desert of southwest Africa the zebra is the engineer who digs the water hole. He seems to smell out water below the surface of canyons long after a rain and dig down two or three feet with his hoofs. Arabian and Australian natives dig similar wells with their hands to get water, but they are not as generous as the coyote or the zebra. They cover their wells to protect them from thirsty animals.

Small waterholes were recognized as the solution to desert survival when chukar partridge from India were released to stock the uplands of deserts in the southwest United States. The "little gray ghosts," as *Desert Magazine* calls these birds, will eat almost anything that grows in the area—insects, grass, weed, and sage seeds. Their favorite food is Russian thistle. They are valuable little game birds, worth preserving in desert areas. They are not only good to eat, but their food habits enable them to find a good living in desert areas. But they must have water regularly. That need was met when thousands of "water guzzlers" were scattered over their range. These concrete or plastic catch basins are rainwater traps. They are located where infrequent rains will fill them quickly and are so constructed that they hold water long after natural pools have dried. Water guzzlers have made it possible not only for chukars to survive but have given the native quail a much larger range.

I don't know how accurate it is to talk about a waterhole truce among desert animals. You will see many accounts of "screams of death at night down at the waterhole." The hungry strong will find the thirsty weak at those gathering places. In time of drought all creatures find their way to water. Game trails converge to the water point from all directions, and they are well traveled. Many tracks are so faint that you seldom see them elsewhere, but in the damp earth at the waterhole you can read the *Who's Who* of the desert world. Seldom do many species drink at the same time. The big fellows assume their rights and wait for no one. Smaller species wait their turn. Each seems to recognize its own social status in the desert world. Each kind knows its place and waits its turn, just as barnyard chickens do when their pecking order is established. Perhaps it is more realistic to talk of recognized discipline at the waterhole than to assume that a desert treaty of peace exists.

We were camped near a bit of open water in the Gobi. Every evening at about sunset and again in early morning flock after flock of sand grouse swept in to drink. No one knows how many miles those birds traveled for their twice-a-day drink, but judging by the scores of them in each flock they must have come from a radius of many miles. During the day some occasionally were seen dusting themselves in the camel trails.

The birds are short-legged and often stand in the water to soak their breast feathers. It's a practical way to carry a drink back to the nestlings who can't yet fly.

The baobab tree, the sheltered canyon, the desert coyote well are all special corners, favored spots in an unfavorable area. Many of the creatures that inhabit those places have no other survival adaptation for desert life than the ability to find a comfortable daytime hide-out. Other species are just opportunists, like the gulls that ganged up on the grasshoppers and saved the crops of the early Mormons in Utah.

Once Edmund C. Jaeger, author of *Desert Wildlife,* saw clouds of geometrid moths over flowering mesquite trees. They had been attracted by the sweet odor of the yellow flowers. Suddenly canyon bats fluttered out from slots in nearby rocks to gobble up the moths. As fast as the first arrivals ate their fill they were replaced by hungry bats. Ordinarily these pygmy bats, *Pipistrellus hesperus,* come out to feed in the dark coolness of early evening, but the unexpected abundance of a moth banquet was an opportunity they didn't miss, despite the heat.

Fish must have permanent water. Springs or permanent pools in otherwise intermittent streams meet their needs in American deserts, where twenty species of fish have been recorded, but seven of them are already extinct. Changes in their food supply and the introduction of exotic species to their special pools are probably respon-sible. Some species are limited to a single spring. Devil's Hole at Ash Meadows, Nevada, has a cave spring of tepid water. It is inhabited by about two hundred pupfish less than an inch long. That seems like a small number of individuals for a species, but so far they seem to be holding their own.

The permanent water of a Sahara irrigating tunnel is also a natural habitat for tiny fish. I've photographed the little minnows in oases five hundred miles from permanent natural streams. Each shallow lake in the Gobi contains a particular species of fish. The lakes are not now connected, although the divides between them are low. The fish of each lake differ from those of neighboring waters. How did the lakes get stocked? Have the fish been isolated so long that separate species developed where they are now found? Were the fish eggs carried from a distance stuck to the feet of birds? Such questions about the desert's fish population are still unanswered.

It is easier to explain the presence of crocodiles in north-flowing rivers of the Sahara. Although none have been reported recently, as far as I know, some of the early explorers reported seeing them. The waters in which small crocodiles were seen could have received them when tropical rivers overflowed their low divides.

The water in desert rivers or irrigating tunnels doesn't differ from that of non-desert areas, so desert fish are more of a curiosity than an example of desert adaptation.

There are habitat specialists, however, which survive because of a specific adjustment. The yucca moth depends on the blossoms of various Spanish bayonette species for its food supply. Without the yucca moth these plants would become extinct. No other agent of natural pollination is known for the yucca. The yucca and the yucca moth are dependent on each other. They have a true symbiotic relationship.

One of the strangest survival tricks is that of the small butterflies found in the Sahara and Middle East deserts. They never leave the cool shade and wind shelter of a certain bush. Each spends its whole lifetime within the shelter of a single bush. Those of the genus *Tarucus* fly continuously among the branches of a zizyphus bush. The tiny *Freyeria galba* lives only in the shelter of a single ononis plant. The plant is only twelve inches in diameter, but the little butterfly keeps on wing in the limited shelter when the flight of other butterflies has been stopped by the wind outside the plant. Surely *Freyeria galba* has attained the peak of isolation for desert survival.

When you get down on your hands and knees to study the minature world of desert insects, you find many fascinating survival patterns. I have spent many lazy hours watching dung beetles in the Gobi, Sahara, and Negev. *Scarabaeus sacre* is the sacred beetle of ancient Egypt. There it represented resurrection and fertility. It is always fascinating to watch the hard-shell-covered creature push a ball of camel dung up-hill on a sand dune. It backs up-hill, pushing the ball with its hind legs. Up, up, up it moves on the steep dune slope. Then the dung ball slips out of the scarab's grasp and rolls back down. Again the beetle backs up-hill with the load, only to lose it again to the force of gravity. So many minutes I've wasted watching those little scavengers! Sometimes I've wondered about the goal the beetle never seemed to reach. I'm not an entomologist, so I never watched the struggle between a scavenger and its ball of dung long enough to see the outcome.

Recently I learned the purpose of the beetle's up-hill struggle. She is compacting a food supply of dung into a tighter and tighter ball for storage. When it is large enough and tight enough she buries the ball of animal droppings. It's the large economy-size food package which will occupy the minimum cupboard space, space that she will have to provide by excavating. In autumn the dung beetle has been known to build a food supply the size of an apple. I've never seen one that big, but everyone I've seen was bigger than the beetle pushing it.

Copris hispanus is one species in which both male and female dig the excavation, some of which are large enough to store half a dozen dung balls. The female lays an egg in each ball and the parents stand guard until the young are grown, ready to be taken above-ground and to go into the world alone.

People often dislike the little scavengers and make derogatory remarks about them and the labor of compacting a ball of such lowly food. An Arab proverb, however, includes them in the wisdom of the world by saying: "In the eyes of a mother dung beetle, her young are as the gazelle." The dung beetles have certainly solved the problem of desert survival. Their hard outer covering prevents loss of moisture and insulates against intense heat. They package their food supply in the most economical shape for handling. Most of their time is spent in comfortable quarters under the ground next to their food.

Another denizen of the desert's miniature world is the ant lion, *Myrmeleon immaculatus*. The ant lion larva was called the "demon of the dust" by the entomologist, W. M. Wheeler. Its cone-shaped pits are easily recognized in fine sand. The creatures lie in the shade at the bottom of the pit until an ant tumbles down the slope, and it is devoured. The pit serves as a trap but it also furnishes shade. The ant lion larva moves with the sun so that he is always on the shady side of the pit.

Some species of ants bring water up from deep strata below their nests. Others, like the harvester ants of California, live in very deep nests well protected against desert heat and drying air. The harvester comes out for short periods only once or twice a day when conditions are favorable and the temperature is within his range of tolerance.

Desert life ranges from ants to antelope. Each species is sometimes abundant in certain localities. However, those localities of abundance are small in size and scarce in quantity when you consider the desert's millions of square miles.

10

Waiting for the Rain

Quickies in the desert plant world wait out long dry spells as seeds. They are adapted to sprout, flower, and set seeds at phenomenal speed as soon as good rains come. Cactus plants have developed tremendous water-storage capacity to last them through long droughts. Other plants drastically reduce evaporation to conserve their moisture when dry winds blow and the skys are not cloudy all day. Each of these survival principles has also been adopted by some animal species.

Toads and frogs in Africa have speeded up that part of their life cycle between egg and adult, although the adults live through drought periods in dormant state. When rain pools form in the arid land these pools swarm with the amphibians. They lay their eggs. The tadpoles hatch, grow their feet, and lose their tails. Before the pools dry up they are adults. They can bury themselves in the mud, which will soon dry and bake hard. Safe beneath the desert surface the animals lie dormant. Their breathing slows down. Their need for moisture is reduced. They can even tolerate dehydration and lose up to

6o percent of their body moisture without injury. When the rains come the water restores their normal weight. The animals wake from their long nap ready to start a new cycle of egg to tadpole to adult and another long nap.

I well remember the first time I heard the desert frogs. We had stayed at a desert swimming hole till sundown. Then we started the long ride on camelback to our quarters. While we rode along a big, yellow harvest moon swung up through the palm trees. The frogs began their evening chorus. The moonlight made slender, romantic shadows from our "ships of the desert," shadows that bobbed and swayed like rowboats on an evening lake. They seemed to match the rhythm of the singing frogs.

In American deserts the spade-foot toad sleeps underground for eight or nine months, but he is a fast operator when the first cloudburst wakes him up. As soon as the storm softens the mud of his sleeping quarters he crawls out and hollers for a girl friend. Eggs are laid at once. Tadpoles hatch in a day or two. In a week they are able to find their way to the mud of the drying pool. In a few weeks their metamorphosis is completed and they are adults. One record time from egg to functioning adult is twenty-eight days.

The spade-foot gets its name from a horny projection on its hind feet. With such well-equipped feet he can back into the mud a foot or so very quickly. He also secretes a gelatinous cover for his body which helps to reduce the loss of body water while he passes the summer in a dormant state.

In the Sonoran and Chihuahan deserts of America, summer rains make warm ponds and shallow lakes of the dry playas. The warm water soon swarms with tiny shrimp. In the Mojave summer rains are rare, never occurring more than a few times per hundred years. Even after such a long dry spell the shrimp appear.

In 1955 there was a cloudburst over the dry bed of Bicycle Lake near Barston on California's Mojave Desert. It was the first rain in a quarter century. Nevertheless, the warm water was soon crowded with tadpole shrimp, fairy shrimp, and clam shrimp. They seemed to appear by magic out of nowhere. During the twenty-five years of drought the shrimp eggs had lain dormant in the salty, parched soil. Like the seeds of quickie plants, they were just waiting for the rains. Bicycle Lake was a real desert pool. The water warmed to 100° F. The eggs hatched and the young became adults and laid more eggs before the lake dried up. Those eggs will wait for the next cloudburst.

The desert tortoise of the Mojave and Sonora might be compared to the cactus in its survival adaptation. Of course, the cactus can't travel twenty feet per minute as the tortoise can. Neither can it sleep out unfavorable weather in a cool burrow. The tortoise, like the cactus, does have a body covering which prevents loss of body water and also makes it difficult for an enemy to attack its vital parts. The animal depends on juicy vegetation for food and water. Apparently its feeding habits supply a surplus of water. Probably some of the food is converted to water, in addition to that obtained from succulent

Fairy shrimp.

In 1955, when rains made Bicycle Lake, California, eighteen inches deep in fresh water, millions of shrimp swarmed in the desert lake. Their eggs had lain dormant for more than twenty years in the dry, caked mud of this playa, but when rain filled the old lake basin, the eggs hatched, and young matured and laid more eggs so that the species could survive another long dry spell.

MERVIN W. LARSON, ARIZONA-SONORA DESERT MUSEUM

Tadpole shrimp.

plants. At any rate, extra water is stored in two sacks just under the shell on its back. These sacks hold about a pint of water, which will last for a season.

On hot summer days the tortoise browses in early morning and late evening. When the desert is too hot for him, he skips a few meals and stays quietly in his burrow. In the pleasant temperatures of spring and fall the tortoise is out during most of the daylight, and like other cold-blooded creatures it becomes more active as the air warms up. In winter it sleeps in its burrow. Then, when spring warms the air and moisture produces abundant vegetation, the animals mate. The leathery, soft-shelled eggs are laid in the sand. The hot sun does the hatching. The youngsters are small copies of the adults and are able to find their own dinners. Although they can survive the desert climate, not many survive the danger of hungry predators.

An Australian frog, *Chiroleptes platycephalus*, can store so much water that thirsty natives use it as a source of drinking water during drought. The flat-headed frog stores water in its bladder, in the body cavity, and in tissues just under the skin. Not only does it drink water, it also absorbs it through the skin. When fully hydrated the creature looks more like a ball than a live frog.

In order to prevent too-rapid loss of water the flat-head burrows into the mud a foot or so at the beginning of dry weather. The mud is soon baked by the sun and gives the animal the protection of a natural adobe house. Native Australians recognize surface indications of the frog's dry-season home and dig him out when they need fresh water.

The animal must dry out now and then to keep in good health and to retain its powers of absorbing water rapidly. In its native habitat, that is taken care of by the normal dry seasons. When a dry, lean animal is suddenly placed in a couple of inches of water it swells and looks like a knobby tennis ball in two minutes. That is probably the fastest recovery from dehydration of any desert-adapted creature.

The body temperature of cold-blooded creatures follows the temperature of the air around them. When the air temperature goes up the body temperature goes up and when the air temperature goes down the body temperature goes down. They can tolerate a wide range between hot and cold, but they do have limits. Beyond those limits, if exposed for any length of time, the animal will die.

We had a number of pets with us most of the summer when we traveled about the Gobi: hawks, owls, crows, etc. They were all predators. We fed them regularly on raw meat. (Incidentally, we presented the feed with chopsticks instead of risking a painful nip on our fingers from those sharp beaks.) In addition to the raw meat, the pets needed some of their more familiar food. Tiny lizards were the easiest creatures for us to catch. In some areas they are fairly numerous and scamper over the rocks to disappear in cracks that always seem too tiny for them. Some of us became clever at catching the little fellows. Once in a while we'd miss the body and catch only the tail. It was most disconcerting. The lizard simply left the tail in our fingers and disappeared among the

These eagles, owls, kites, and ravens were some of our pets in the Gobi Desert. They were voracious meat eaters that our mechanic fed by using chopsticks.

AUTHOR'S PHOTO

rocks. This self-amputation doesn't hurt the lizard at all, for it soon grows a new tail. I've never heard whether or not the new tail also can be amputated automatically. At least this ability allows the lizard one error in avoiding predators.

Ability to lose the tail painlessly is protection against one hazard of the lizard's desert environment but does not help against the greater hazard of desert temperatures. Some authorities believe that the creatures are most active when the air is 96° to 100° F. but are prostrate when it reaches 104° to 116°. During the intense heat of midday they must stay in good shade. If forced out onto the stove-heat of the burning desert, they die in a few minutes. None can live when the desert floor is 180° F.

At least one species, the spiny lizard of California, has a special organ, a third eye between its two visual organs. This extra eye is considered vestigial, although it has a cornea, a lens, a retina, and a nerve to the brain. It does function as a warning organ to tell the lizard when it should seek shade from the hot sun. If this parietal eye is covered or removed the lizard gets careless about staying in the sun too long.

The only time I ever saw a gila monster he was in deep shade under a bush in Monument Valley. It was a hot afternoon. I can't remember what business I had, all bent over and prowling under bushes, but suddenly I saw the brute not over three feet from my foot. *Heloderma horridum* didn't move a muscle but stared at me with his unfriendly eyes. He was certainly the most *horridum* looking creature I have ever seen. He must have been

Gila monster, ugly but edible.

MERVIN W. LARSON, ARIZONA-SONORA DESERT MUSEUM

about 1½ feet long; nearly half of that was tail.

If I had been hungry and had had a club or other weapon handy, the thick tail of *Heloderma horridum* would have made a good meal. To get it I would have had to kill the monster, because he is one lizard who can't self-amputate his tail. The tail is useful to the lizard as a reserve food supply when he has poor luck finding eggs, young birds, rabbits, or juicy rodents.

The gila monster and the horned lizard are both protected by law in Arizona. I believe the monster is the first venomous reptile to have legal protection. He's fast when he's hungry or aroused, despite his awkward looks. When he bites he hangs on like a bulldog and tries to chew the victim. His poison glands are at the back of his mouth, so unless he can chew your flesh with his back teeth he can't poison you. Even if he bites you the chances are good that you can tear yourself away before his poison gets into your system.

In Australia another lizard, *Moloch horridus,* prefers a diet of ants. In a rain, the rough skin of this species is like blotting paper. It absorbs water quickly to restore the animal's water balance.

"Get out of the sun" is a command obeyed by all desert creatures. Big or little, cold-blooded or warm-blooded, none violate that order on pain of death. Snakes and lizards hide in rock crevices or any other shade. Some are especially adapted for burrowing into loose sand. Species of snakes and lizards found as far apart as the deserts of Arabia and California can close their nostrils, mouth, and eyes to keep out the sand as they dig

This desert lizard, thhaihi, *can quickly disappear into the sand by vibrating its body in a rapid shimmy.*

ARABIAN AMERICAN OIL COMPANY

in out of the heat. In the Arabian Desert a small lizard "shimmies" its body into the sand. Arabs call the little fellow *thhaihi.*

In the desert plant world, drastic reduction of evaporation is accomplished by shedding leaves or whole branches. Among animals, estivation accomplishes the same result. To estivate means to pass the summer in a dormant state. It is a more drastic slowdown than sleeping.

Snails are as efficient estivators as any animals I know. These creatures are plentiful in North Africa during late winter and early spring. They formed the staple food of the prehistoric, Old Stone Age people we call the Snail Eaters. These people left huge mounds of snail shells and campfire ashes on the banks of narrow watercourses. When we were studying those mounds we collected live snails for our dinner once or twice and sent hundreds to America for study. Dr. Frank C. Baker at the University of Illinois found that most of the living species were the same as those eaten by the Stone Age people.

Snails inhabit the arid lands wherever night dew is common. At times their abundance is almost beyond belief. I recall a letter from my friend, Hal Denny, a war correspondent for *The New York Times.* From Morocco he wrote that trains were being delayed by snails. Millions of them were moving across the railway right of way. Of course engineers wouldn't stop for such insignificant creatures. The wheels of the engine crushed the snails, but their juicy bodies "greased" the rails and made the drive-wheels spin. The engineers used up their supply of track sand long before they could cross the migrating horde.

The snails are vegetarians. When summer heat begins to dry the air they crawl into rock crevices, pull their juicy bodies back into their shells and seal the opening with a membrane. Deep in rock shade they become dormant, completely inactive but still alive. When summer heat is over and winter showers return, the moisture softens the seal on the shells. The snail emerges to satisfy its voracious appetite and lay its eggs to guarantee the next generation.

In 1846 some specimens of estivating desert snails, *Helix desertorum,* were glued to a display in the British Museum in London. Four years later a conchologist (student of shells,) put them in water. One snail was still alive. It came out of estivation and was normally active.

There are estivators among higher animal forms also. A ground squirrel found in the deserts of Turkestan both estivates and hibernates. He is active only during the three or four months when he can feed on green vegetation. That keeps him dormant through the dry summer and allows only a short break in fall before he has to go to sleep for the winter.

Most warm-blooded creatures keep down the loss of body water by reducing their activity during the heat of the day. It is possible that the big ears of the jackrabbit and of the little fennec or desert fox, *Vulpes zerda,* serve to cool the animals as well as to sharpen their hearing. The veins in their thin ears bring the blood close to the surface, where it cools more easily than it would deeper in the fur-covered body.

Evaporation of water is the most effective way for an animal to reduce its body temperature. Some cool down by sweating as man does. Others—dogs and birds, for example—pant. They evaporate the moisture of their lungs by heavy breathing. Some animals of Australia increase their saliva as the temperature rises. They can't spit on themselves, of course, but they do spread the saliva with their tongue. The koala, *Phascolarctos cinereus,* a little Australian marsupial, begins to lick its paws and rub saliva on its face when its body temperature reaches 99° F. The Australian wallaby pants and has free-flowing saliva with which it washes its whole body. When its temperature reaches 101° F., saliva flows very fast. If there is not enough to keep body temperature below 103°F., the hind legs become partially paralyzed. This condition is called heat staggers.

Most birds can fly to cool shelter just as animals go into rock-protected cavities or dig underground. Many of them have made other concessions to the desert heat. In the Sahara many birds are the same species as those found nesting in more humid and cooler parts of the Mediterranean basin. The desert birds, however, have made two major adjustments to heat and dryness. They limit the size of their families and they have those families weeks earlier than their non-desert relatives. The small families are necessary because the parents must travel farther and search longer to get enough food for the hungry youngsters, and because of the heat they must take a long "noon hour" in the middle of the day. Occasionally you'll see a bird in a bush trying to keep cool by panting with open beak and feathers fluffed out to create dead air insulation from the heat.

Nesting early means that the young are hatched when desert vegetation is most abundant and insects most plentiful. Even with food supplies at their desert peak, the scarcity of areas where food is abundant gives the parent birds a busy time trying to keep the gaping mouths full.

Spring in the American southwest deserts is the time of blooming. That is when the birds are nesting there. But the same species nest in central Mexico. There the desert blooms in June and July. The Mexican birds adjust to the time of abundance and don't mate until early summer.

Where there are no predictable rains with corresponding abundance, the bird inhabitants must be as alert for rain as the seeds of desert quickies. Small, insect-eating birds in Australia mate for years without ever nesting. The instant a heavy rain falls they build a nest, lay their eggs, and start incubating them. Have those birds some secret way of knowing rain will come and the desert air will fill with insects for baby food? Or does the sight and feel of many raindrops stimulate their reproductive cycle? We don't know.

Some American ornithologists believe that lack of Vitamin A keeps the birds sterile. They get that vitamin from fresh, green vegetation. When there are no rains there are no fresh salads for the birds: no green salad, no Vitamin A, and no nesting birds.

Gordon W. Gullion made a study of Gambel's quail near Searchlight, Nevada. There was only 0.66 inches of rain there in 1955–6. There were practically no young birds that year. Two years earlier, 1953–54 was a wet year with 4.8 inches of rain. In that nesting period there were 632 young quail for every 100 adults. He also found that adults may or may not pair off every spring. Mating seemed to depend on their health in spring. In dry years the winter covey stays together all summer.

In Texas, the bobwhite has similar habits. If good rains produce good vegetation and a good crop of insects, the quail may raise two broods in the season. The parents leave the first brood with a bachelor as baby-sitter, who guides them in growing up and learning the tricks of desert survival.

There are many other interesting desert birds. The funny-looking road runner looks like a long-legged, long-tailed chicken as he races ahead of your car on a dusty road. He's good at catching snakes and lizards. He doesn't care if a snake is too big for his throat. The road runner swallows as much as he can and runs around with the snake's tail hanging from his beak. As the swallowed end of the snake is digested the bird will gulp down a few more inches of his dangling dinner.

Another interesting bird of the southwest deserts is the rock wren, *Troglodytes obsoletus* (some authorities call it *T. salpinctes*). It has a wide range in western North America and British Columbia to lower California, Mexico. It also nests from near-sea-level cliffs up to near-timber-line. That range includes a great deal of desert, but perhaps we should consider the rock wren as a very

Roadrunner with a coral snake in its beak. This bird is known as the clown of the desert.

MERVIN W. LARSON, ARIZONA-SONORA DESERT MUSEUM

adaptable species rather than one especially suited to deserts, although it is common in arid lands.

Creatures that spend their summers in high altitudes and northern latitudes move to warm deserts for the winter, but southern desert-dwellers are year-round residents. They inhabit sandstone and lava cliffs, steep granite rocks or clay-walled gullies. Any area with many cracks and crevices, narrow crypts, or little caves is ideal for the long-billed hunter of insects. His flatish head and body and his short legs enable him to go in and out among the rocks like a little caveman. His toes are long and sharp-clawed. Their wide span enables the little fellow to get a good hold on walls and even on overhanging rocks. His long bill lets him probe the rock crevices well beyond the reach of other birds.

The rock wren's rocky habitat offers numerous cool cavities. He can do his food hunting when the open desert is far too hot for other insect eaters. Some observers seem to think his diet of spiders and crevice-haunting juicy insects make it unnecesary for him to drink water very often. It is more likely that he finds drinking water several times a day back among the rocks and tiny caves he constantly explores. Such hidden cisterns hold water weeks and months after a desert rain. Although they are hidden from the human desert traveler, I'm certain the rock wren finds them.

The nesting habits of this bird differ from any I have ever seen. No two nests are alike. Observers have found them at ground level and fifty feet above the desert floor. The nest itself is a cup-like hollow of twigs, grass, and rootlets lined with finer grass, hair, or shredded bark. It is located in a rock crack or crevice. Across the rocky entrance the bird builds a wall of flat pebbles, chips, or spalls of stone. The stone fragments are carried to the site in the bird's bill. Below the wall there is always a path paved with similar bits of rock. Sometimes the "path" is only a heap rather than a real pavement. Perhaps the bits of material in front of the wall are pieces that have been rejected and should not be considered as part of a path at all. Whether or not the pint of stones found in front of the nest site represents a walkway, the bird is well named—rock wren in English and cave dweller in Latin.

The strangest adaptation of a desert bird has nothing to do with intense summer heat and low humidity although it is a way of waiting for the rain. Instead of flying to a warm winter habitat, the poorwill, *Phalaenoptilus nattalli,* actually hibernates. The bird is a small, pale relative of the common eastern whippoorwill, which inhabits the arid lands of the western United States.

Edmund C. Jaeger, author of *Desert Wildlife,* was the first to make a scientific report on the hibernating poorwill. On December 29, 1946, he found the bird "asleep" in a rock hollow thirty inches above the sand floor of a narrow canyon in the Chuckawalla Mountains, in the Colorado Desert of California. Dr. Jaeger handled the bird and stroked its feathers without rousing it. He put a standard bird band on its leg and returned every week to weigh it and make careful notes about its condition.

The normal body temperature of the poorwill when it is awake is 106° F. The temperature of the dormant body of the poorwill hibernating in the Chuckawalla Mountains was down to 64.4° F. The bird's heartbeat was too faint to detect. So was its breathing. A mirror held in front of its nostrils collected no moisture. Each week, however, there was a slight loss of weight. The bird was in true hibernation, with drastically slowed down body processes.

Sometimes Jaeger found it with one eye open. Light from his little fountain-pen-type flashlight didn't bother the bird at all. In the spring the poorwill was gone from the canyon crevice, but it was back and hibernating again in the winters of 1947–48, 1948–49, and 1949–50.

Isn't it strange that such an interesting desert survival adaptation wasn't reported until 1949? Surely others must have seen the hibernating insect-eaters. When you think of all the millions of birdwatchers in America it seems impossible that such an event could go unreported.

Unreported, yes, but it was not unobserved. Hopi Indians called the poorwill "the sleeping one." Surely they had noticed its hibernation. When Jaeger asked his Navaho friends where the poorwill goes in winter they said "up in the rocks."

After Dr. Jaeger's report got into print other observers sent him accounts of their observations. In 1953 a report from Tucson, Arizona, recorded a hibernating poorwill with a body temperature down to 55.7° F. That same year a dormant bird was noted in Joshua Tree National Monument.

One observer, A. L. McCasland of California, reported that he had seen thirty-five or forty hibernating birds during the winters of 1931–32 and 1933–34. He found them in dry giant catcuses on the San Pedro River near Mammoth, Arizona. Although the pulp of the saguaro rots, the hard ribs do not. The birds had found a cavity for hibernation and covered themselves with the dry pulp.

Credit for the real "first" in modern times, however, belongs to the children of the one-room school in Wheeler Springs, Nevada. In 1909 the "schoolhouse" was a tent, and all the pupils were from the Wheeler family. Maud A. Minthorn was the teacher. After hearing of Dr. Jaeger's discovery she wrote to him about her experience at the Wheeler School.

The children told her about a bird that slept in a hole in a bank near the school. Their statement was hard for Miss Minthorn to accept.

"Oh, yes!" the children insisted. "It sleeps there every winter. We'll show you."

As adults will, Miss Minthorn probably reasoned that the children were either mistaken or were trying to get an hour away from the classroom. Finally, one day in April Miss Minthorn followed the children to the hibernator's den. The story was no hoax. The poorwill was there, as the children had said.

Wheeler Springs, Nevada, is at six thousand feet elevation. Snow comes early there, and Maud Minthorn believes that the poorwill must spend seven months hibernating in that arid land.

Children are so often better observers than adults. Those Wheeler children had scientific information thirty-seven years before the facts reached scientific publications.

11

The Champions of Desert Survival

Camels and a dozen genera of rodents have solved the problems of desert survival so well that they must be rated the real experts on life in arid lands. The camel of Africa and Asia may sometimes weigh more than half a ton. The jerboa of Egypt or the kangaroo rat of American deserts weighs about an ounce. Regardless of size each has developed ways to keep in water balance. Each maintains its body temperature within the deadly extremes of desert climate.

Nineteen hundred years ago the Roman naturalist Gaius Plinius Secundus (Pliny the Elder) stated that camels store water in their stomachs to last for days on long desert marches. Naturalists and travelers, even zoologists who should have checked the statement have repeated that mistake for nineteen hundred years!

The camel *can* go several days without drinking in summer deserts. He *can go months* without water if he is loafing in good winter pasture. Such long periods between his drinks do not prove that he has stored water for the drought. They do mean that his body has ad-

Dr. Knut Schmidt-Nielsen hoisting a camel to a steelyard (above the photograph) for a weigh-in to check the water loss since the animal's last drink.

DR. KNUT SCHMIDT-NIELSEN

justed to the demands of the desert climate in many practical ways. I was just about to say, "every possible way," when I remembered Pliny's mistake. There are "possible ways" which the camel doesn't use. Some of them are used by the desert rodents and some future scientists may still discover other ways not now known.

In 1953–54 Drs. Bodil and Knut Schmidt-Nielson made a study of camel physiology for UNESCO at the desert research station in Beni-Abbès, Algeria. They weighed the animals before and after drinking. They measured the water they drank. They measured the moisture lost in breathing and the oxygen used by the animals. They studied blood samples and did laboratory studies on the stomachs of dead camels. The zoologists collected more scientific data about the physiology of camels than had been gathered by all observers in the world during the nineteen hundred years since Pliny made his error.

Stories about travelers and camel men who have killed their animals and drunk the contents of their stomachs to keep from dying of thirst are true. What they drank were rich digestive juices. Nourishing stuff, to be sure, and it contains moisture which helps to restore a dehydrated man. But it is not water any more than blood is water. Drinking the camel's blood would restore the thirsty traveler just as well. In fact, the soldiers of the famous desert warrior Genghis Khan opened veins to drink the blood of their horses when water was gone.

The Schmidt-Nielsons found the so-called water-sacs in the camel's rumin (first stomach) contained masticated food and not much liquid. The capacity of the rumin's little wall sacs is only 5 to 7 liters. That's not enough storage capacity to account for the 103 liters a camel can drink in ten minutes *after* eight days without water in late June, *not before* the deprivation period.

When man dehydrates his blood thickens. His heart has to work harder to keep up his circulation. Even 5 percent dehydration slows down his body processes and seriously lowers his efficiency. Fifteen percent dehydration in air temperature of 90° F., or higher is probably fatal to man.*

---

*A Mexican, Pablo Valencia, recovered from 25 percent dehydration, but that case is the fantastic exception to all the rules and all the statistics on dehydration. For details see Chapter XIX, *The Desert World*, by Alonzo W. Pond. Thomas Nelson, New York, 1962.

The camel loses moisture from its body but very little of it from the blood. The near-normal blood does not overwork the camel's heart or slow down the body processes. The result is that the animal can dehydrate up to 30 percent of its body weight without permanent damage. The lost water can be *replaced* in a few minutes, although it may be a day or so before it is evenly distributed throughout the body. In addition to dehydration tolerance, the animal has many other advantages for survival in the heat of waterless wastelands.

Although he cannot store water he can store heat. Normal body temperature in the camel ranges about 12°, from 94° F. to 106° F. In man the normal range is only a degree or less above and below 98.6° F. That means that a camel can warm up during the day to 106° F. without sweating and cool down during the night and early morning without affecting his body processes.

Heat flows downhill. The steeper the grade the faster it flows. It is a steeper slope from 120° F. to 98.6° F. than it is from 120° F. to 106° F. Therefore, at midday in the desert during summer, the camel absorbs less heat than man. He has less to get rid of and does not have to use so much water in sweating. He can make a little water go a long way. Of course, his wool coat also insulates his body against the hot desert air. It lets the sweat evaporate slowly and do a more efficient job of cooling.

The dromedary camel, which is most common in the hot deserts of Africa and Arabia, has long, slender legs. They carry the bulk of his body several feet up above the desert floor. It's cooler up there than it is close to the ground. The easygoing, slow motion of a camel's gait generates much less body heat than speedy action does. Although the animal may not be able to get into any shade where he lives, his other advantages enable him to conserve his body moisture and get the most benefit from his sweat.

As we have said, he doesn't store water for his long journey. He does store food, however. When he is loafing in rich winter pasture his extra food is converted into fat. That accumulates in the hump on his back. The Bactrian camel of Asia has two humps joined by a low valley. If you are buying a camel for a desert journey be sure to pick one with as big and firm a hump or humps as possible. You may have to cross long stretches without any pasture for your camel, or the pasture may be so poor that you don't want to wait while the animal gets enough to eat. At such times the camel begins to live off his hump. The stored fat will be converted to energy to keep him going.

Some people have pointed out that the camel's body actually produces water because when fat is converted into energy it uses oxygen. Some of the oxygen combines with hydrogen of the fat to produce water. That is true, but the extra oxygen must be brought into the camel's body through his lungs. When he breathes he loses moisture from his lungs. The extra breathing uses just about as much water as was produced in converting the fat of the hump to energy. There is no water surplus from converting the hump.

No matter how hard we try to rationalize that camels

store water, the facts just will not support this wishful thinking. In all their experiments the Schmidt-Nielsens found that camels drink only to *replace* water lost since the last drink. If the animals had been in good, lush pasture where the vegetation had all the moisture the animals needed, they would refuse drinking water when it was offered. They would refuse even if they had not been to the well for weeks.

In hot weather, when camels are fed on dry dates—not the juicy ones we eat but those that are hard and dry as peanut shells—they will drink every three or four days. Circus men tell me they water camels every day and "they drink as much as a horse of similar weight." Whenever they do drink they take in just enough water to repay their water deficit. They can't put any water in a savings account, but their "bank" tolerates a 25 percent or 30 percent overdraft before stopping credit—killing them.

Several desert rodents have solved the problem of desert survival by adaptations entirely different from those developed in camels. The *Dipodomys*, or kangaroo rat, of the American deserts, the jerboas and gerbils of Africa and the Near East, the marsupial kangaroo mice and pitchi-pitchis of Australia are examples of nearly a dozen unrelated look-alikes. Long, strong hind legs and short, weak front legs make them look like tiny kangaroos. The head, nose, and small furry body give them a superficial resemblance to rats and mice. Despite their lack of family relationship all have met desert harshness in the same way. It is a little like the resemblance of desert lilies—

Spanish bayonettes—to the cactuses. Each group of plants has sharp spines, water-storage capacity, and a tough outer coating to prevent evaporation.

The American kangaroo rat and the Egyptian jerboa have been so thoroughly studied that they may be used as examples of desert adaptation for the whole group of desert rodents. Perhaps their greatest enemies are the predators. Hawks, and owls, wolves and foxes, big lizards, any creature that enjoys a juicy morsel of fresh meat is always ready to gobble up a kangaroo rat or one of his look-alikes.

The little fellows can't battle those enemies with tooth and claw, but they are equipped for a fast getaway. Their clever dodging leaves the enemy in open-mouthed bewilderment when he expected to close his teeth on an evening snack. Those strong, kangaroo-like hind legs can move the kangaroo rat twenty feet per second. That is fairly close to the four-minute mile. Not bad for a little fellow, when you realize that each "step" covers two feet of ground, many times his own body length.

His extra long tail has a tuft of hair at the end. It's big enough to act like an aeroplane rudder when he's in mid-air. He can make a zag to the left or a zig to the right between takeoff and landing, even a full right-angle turn at the apogee of his leap. Such agility often saves his life, but not always. The little fellows are staple diet for desert predators, although many survive.

All of the group are warm-blooded creatures and must keep their body temperature within limits. None of them can sweat to lower that temperature. They have, accord-

Banner-tailed kangaroo rat, Dipodomys spectabilis. This little animal is so well adapted to desert living that it can live on dry seeds alone. Its long, tufted tail enables it to turn sharply at the top of a long jump and so avoid an enemy.

DR. KNUT SCHMIDT-NIELSEN

Kangaroo rat in its burrow. Underground he is insulated from desert surface heat, and moisture from his breathing keeps the burrow comfortably humid.

MERVIN W. LARSON, ARIZONA-SONORA DESERT MUSEUM

ingly, adopted a way of life that does not expose them to
the stress of desert heat. They live in burrows dug a foot
and a half below the hot desert floor, where it is cool
during the day. At night, when the desert floor cools off,
they come out of their cozy nests to scamper about collecting seeds. Pouches in the cheeks or in the throat—
gullar pouches—are handy pockets to fill with seeds to be
carried to the animals' storage pits.

Big eyes are satisfactory for night vision. They are
able to see their way from burrow to feeding ground and
back without difficulty. The large *bulla tempani,* the
bone just below the ear, magnifies faint sounds of the
"silent" desert night and helps keep the animal out of
reach of hungry enemies.

Dr. John P. Kirmiz found four different floor plans for
the burrows of jerboas living in the Egyptian Sahara.
These enabled the jumpers to live in their own comfortable microclimate regardless of outside heat. Long before man brought air conditioning to the desert, jerboas
were controlling the temperature and humidity of their
living quarters.

The burrows used during Egypt's rainy winter are on
side hills, so there is no danger of flooding. In summer
they are less elevated and are placed near open fields
where some vegetation is found. The simplest burrow is
the side-hill tunnel, about five feet long, with the end
about four feet below the surface.

Kirmiz calls the second type the angular burrow. It
has an acute angle which checks air circulation. It is
generally about 7½ feet long and ends 5 feet below the
surface.

A third type, the zig-zag burrow, has a couple of sharp angles in its length of six and a half feet, with the chamber almost that far below the surface.

The fourth is called a hooked burrow. The main tunnel turns back on itself like a fishhook. It is about 13 feet long and ends 2½ feet below the surface. It also has an abandoned branch which was used during excavation. This branch is plugged with dirt but is easily opened if necessary as an emergency exit. Temperature and humidity can be controlled by modifying the tunnel length with different size plugs. In winter the burrow is not sealed, but in summer the plug keeps out warm air and snakes. The winter nest also has a cotton wool lining, Kirmiz says, for added warmth.

The jerboa does not estivate nor hibernate but is active nearly every night during the climatic calm. That is from 9 P.M. to 6 A.M. During the day, surface temperatures may range from 72° F. to 95° F., while within the burrow the range is from 85° F. to 91° F., a six-degree range inside compared to a twenty-three degree range outside. The air-conditioned shelter also has much higher humidity. Inside there is two to five times as much moisture as above ground. That is extremely important because the animal loses body moisture when it breathes dry air. When the air breathed in has as much moisture as that exhaled there is no water loss.

In the Kara Kum Desert of the Soviet Union, gerbil burrows only four inches below the surface were found to be 31° F. cooler at midday than the surface.

Kirmiz says that the jerboa of Egypt does not store food in the burrow but eats sprouting vegetation or roots.

When these are absent he lives on dry seeds.

W. T. Shaw, who studied kangaroo rats in the San Joaquin Valley, California, found one animal had 875 temporary storage caches in an area of five square yards. These were shallow and were used only during the harvest season. Shaw marked the seeds with Mercurochrome so they could be traced to the main storage pits.

In southern Arizona, another student, Hudson Reynolds, found that the Merriam kangaroo rat collected marked seeds from the feeding station to bury in caches fifty feet away. Later they were dug up. Not all of them reached the permanent food cache. When the rain came, whole clusters of seeds which the animal had failed to move sprouted at the temporary storage sites.

Certainly the most truly desertic adaptation of any animal is the ability of the kangaroo rat to live on dry seeds alone and maintain water balance.

Bagnold (see Chapter 4) found desert rodents alive and healthy fifty miles downwind from any vegetation in a waterless area of the Libyan Desert. He concluded that they depended on seeds carried to them by the wind. Possibly some seeds are also present from the crop produced at the time of the last rain, even though that may have been more than a decade past.

The quantities of seeds from desert plants seem almost inexhaustible. Even though it may be years between seed-sprouting rains, those rare seed crops are big enough to last the seed-eaters for years and still leave enough to produce the next crop. Lloyd Tevis, Jr., who worked in Coachella Valley, California, estimated that plants must produce 1.45 billion (1,450,000,000) seeds to the acre in a dry year. His estimate was based on the storage of seeds by harvester ants. One ant colony collected seven thousand seeds per day!

Regardless of where the seeds may come from, the desert rodents can live on dry seeds alone. In the laboratory they have not only lived on dry food and nothing else, they have even gained weight on that waterless diet and maintained their water balance for years.

The secret is that the little animals manufacture all the water they need from their dry food. The process of digesting the carbohydrates of the seeds releases hydrogen. It combines with oxygen to produce the needed body water. Other animals produce water that way, too, but only the desert rodents produce enough to keep themselves in water balance and have enough left over to eliminate body wastes.

There is another secret process that guarantees survival for the desert rodents. The kidneys of the kangaroo rat eliminate waste urea in a 22.8 percent concentration. Human kidneys are only about one quarter as efficient. The rodent's feces are also 20 percent drier than the solid waste of similar, non-desert animals (such as white rats used in laboratory experiments). The kangaroo rats also lose only half as much moisture in breathing as white rats do.

All these efficient body processes of the desert rodents, added to their moisture-saving habits of life, make them the most truly desert-adapted of all desert animals. Man, of course, cannot alter his body chemistry to imitate either the camel or the kangaroo rat for survival in sun and sand. But he can adopt many of the living habits by which the animals have increased their mastery of their arid environment.

12

Man in the Desert —
Man of the Desert

Man can live in the desert, but no race nor group of human beings has evolved any physical adaptation for life in arid lands. None has improved the efficiency of body processes for life in the desert as the camel and kangaroo rat have done. Almost all individuals can acclimate to the desert regardless of where they were born and raised. Some can adjust to the arid environment in two or three days. Some function well a week after arrival. Others may take three weeks before their bodies work efficiently. A few never adjust.

Such acclimatization is similar to the adjustment your body makes in temperate climates between summer and a sudden winter. Every change in the weather affects your body functions and requires adjustment, a sort of tune-up for the changed conditions. That is what we mean by acclimatization. It is quite different from the camel's ability to store heat or the functioning of the kangaroo rat's efficient kidneys.

All human beings must keep their body temperature close to the normal level of 98.6° F. All generate body heat when they exercise. All must get rid of the extra heat by evaporating sweat. Each foot-pound of work a man does generates the same number of calories whether his skin is red, white, yellow, or black. Every one hundred calories of surplus heat generated by the body or absorbed from the air, sun, or ground must be balanced by the evaporation of six ounces of sweat.

Although human beings cannot change their physiology for life in the desert, they can make environmental changes such as building a house or wearing clothes. They can adopt living habits that fit activity to favorable periods of the day. Perhaps most important of all, one can make a mental adjustment to the arid lands. Without the psychological adjustment you may live all your life *in* the desert and never be a man *of* the desert.

Oasis dwellers are in the desert but not necessarily of the desert. They depend on water from distant points to irrigate their crops and provide drinking water. That water may come from wells, irrigating tunnels, or surface rivers. In any case, the water fell as rain or snow far from the place in which it is used. Some city dwellers in American deserts, and the whole population of Egypt, live on water from outside the desert. Adequate water and insulated dwellings remove most of the stress of desert living for oasis dwellers.

Many oasis people never leave the irrigated acres. They are as terrified of the desert trails as any stranger from temperate lands. Such people do live from birth to death in the desert. But never are they of the desert.

Someone has said that American desert cities are parasites on the economy of a prosperous nation. Not only does the water on which they depend come from mountains of other states, but the money to build the dams and irrigating systems comes from taxes on non-desert inhabitants.

Native Australians, Kalahari Bushmen, the Mongols of the Gobi, the Tuaregs of the Sahara, the Sulaba tribe of Arabia, and the Indians of desert America have all accepted a way of life suitable to the desert world. They live in the desert and are of the desert as well. They accept the desert's limitations as well as its bounty. They like it there.

Non-desert natives find the desert a strange world. It terrifies some, making them cringe in fear. It seizes others with its beauty and makes them mystics. Three of the world's great religions, Judaism, Christianity, and Islam were born in the desert, and so was that of the Navajo Indians. Life is reduced to simple questions and positive answers in the desert. There is no *if*. There are no *maybes*. You have water and you live, or you don't have water and you die. You conform to desert conditions and succeed, or you compromise and fail. There is no in-between. Those who have learned to meet the rugged, uncompromising conditions of the desert world seem to enjoy a freedom of the spirit not often found elsewhere. That freedom comes with the understanding of survival needs and the complete acceptance of the desert rules.

The naked little Bushman of the Kalahari, the dignified, flowing-robed Tuareg of the Sahara, the yurt-dwelling Mongol horseman of the Gobi, and the oil-rich sheik of Arabia never fight the harshness of the desert. Like the cactus, they make certain that they don't run out of water. Like the camel, slow-motion is their custom. Like the gazelle and the kangaroo rat, they rest in shade at midday. Like the butterfly, *Freyeria galba,* they seek shelter from the wind.

The Australian native, the Kalahari Bushman, the Sulaba tribesman of Arabia are all famous for their ability to survive in the harshest desert. All have the same kind of eyes and ears and nose and taste buds as you have. They have the same sense of touch and the same capable mind and memory as you and I. The big difference is that these people of empirical cultures constantly depend on their senses and their memory. Long and constant practice keeps them alert and makes them aware of details you and I never know exist. Like the animals they hunt, they have a thorough, practical knowledge of the territory in which they move. And like the animals, they stay within the boundaries of their familiar territory.

If they move from camp to waterhole or follow a game trail or hunt a tasty tuber these people note all sights and sounds and smells. Their computer-like memories hold the data for months and years. When needed, the facts are available to remind them where they saw a food plant growing whose bulb is now ready to eat; where they stored an ostrich-egg shell full of water to use when they were thirsty; whether the sound they hear now means friend or enemy, a food animal approaching or a predator to be avoided.

Water is the chief concern of desert people, as it is for

Colocynth *or colocynth apple grows on a vine and resembles a watermelon but it is poisonous, causing violent vomiting. Kalahari Desert natives recognize a similar fruit, which supplies them with water to drink, but even they claim that some individual plants are too bitter to eat.*

Close-up view of the colocynth.

Lecanora esculenia, *also called desert manna by the Italians of Libya, is found far out in the Libyan Desert, a part of the great Sahara.*

all desert life. Those of empirical cultures live so close to nature that they have never had a surplus of food, water, and energy to convert into such capital investment as wells and irrigation projects. They are almost as dependent on natural water basins as the birds. Some follow the technique of the coyote and dig shallow wells in moist places. Good trackers in Arabia appear to know the signs and dig in the dunes for water. Probably their special knowledge includes the memory of where the rains fell recently. It also recognizes that water soaks down only a few inches on one side of the dunes and runs off the surface entirely on the hard side.

Australians dig near water-indicator plants and moisture-holding depressions. When they leave their "wells" they cover them with natural debris so skillfully that even experienced white men never find them without the aid of a native tracker. Kalahari Bushmen store water in ostrich-egg shells and bury them for later use. They also dig "sip wells."

Sip wells are an extremely temporary but excellent emergency source of water. The Bushman scoops out a hollow, to reach moist earth. Usually it is about eighteen

Guides in the Arabian Desert have an uncanny knowledge about where they can strike water with a little digging.

inches deep. One end of a long, hollow reed is wrapped with grass to make a coarse strainer. The grass bundle, with reed protruding, is buried at the bottom of the hollow. The free end of the reed sticks up in the air. Sand is packed tight around the grass ball. In half an hour or so the well digger starts to suck on the reed. The suction creates a partial vacuum in the grass strainer around the buried end of the reed. Water seeps to the reed and is "pumped" up to the operator's mouth.

After swallowing a few times to satisfy his thirst, the water-man, or more often water-woman, puts another reed in his or her mouth. As water is sucked up it is squirted through the second reed to an egg shell or other container.

The amount of water produced from a sip well is considerable when the well is operated efficiently. The classic record is that of one "Bush" MacIntyre and a companion who went into the Kalahari to dig a new well. A Bushman woman kept herself, the two men, and their four donkeys supplied with water until the permanent well was completed. The woman used all the suction her lungs could produce, so that her cheeks were drawn almost together at each pull on the well reed.

More prosperous desert peoples have used their surplus time, food, and energy to dig permanent wells. Out in the western Gobi an enterprising bandit hauled water, food, and tools to a waterless stretch and hired men to dig a good well. It made a shorter trail for commercial caravans. The bandit was not wholly public-spirited, of course. Occasionally he raided a rich prize, but he allowed most caravans to pass unmolested. Enough of them always got through safely to make the short route a reasonably good gamble without killing the goose that laid the golden egg.

Once in the Sahara, when there was no winter work for laborers in the oasis, I was invited by a sheik to see the start of a new irrigating tunnel. All laborers in the community were invited to the groundbreaking. Men brought their digging hoes. Women brought their water jars. The men swung their hoes and deepened the trench as they sang. The women carried water from a well to keep down the dust. Others tended cooking fires and prepared a feast. Later the workmen would continue the digging when there was no other source of income. In four or five years, using this surplus labor, the sheik would have created a new source of water. That water he could sell to irrigate more garden plots.

Wells and irrigation projects in oases relieve the oasis dwellers of the most severe desert stresses. But both oasis dwellers and naked wild men must conserve their sweat and their energy in desert heat. Both seek shade from late morning to early evening in summer heat. I well remember the oasis city of Biskra, Algeria, in June. Before noon each day the streets were as deserted as those of any small town where "they roll up the sidewalks at night." Like the natives we went to our quarters in the thick-walled hotel. The windows were closed. Heavy drapes kept out the sun. We lay on the floor in light pajamas and dozed all afternoon.

About six o'clock muffled street noises reached our room. We opened the window drapes. Down on the main street cafe waiters were moving chairs and tables out to the sidewalks. Some were soaking the pavement with water from garden hoses. As the first drops of water struck the hot blacktop pavement thin fog rose a few inches and disappeared in the dry air. In half an hour the streets of

Biskra were cool and noisy with strolling crowds. Business places were again open. Gone was the midday silence. The desert town was as alive and busy as it had been during the early-morning market hours.

Out on the open desert the story is similar. The caravans that started their day near sunrise make camp by 10 A.M. Most of the people rest, rolled up in their wool burnooses (cape-like robes) to insulate their bodies from the heat and let their sweat evaporate efficiently while they sleep on the ground in the shade of tents with the sides rolled up.

At a Tuareg camp the reed-mat walls are rolled away from the leather tents to let the air circulate beneath the black shade. When the sun swings well to the west you can hear the rhythmic thump of a pestle pounding millet in a wooden mortar. Servants are getting ready for the evening meal.

In the Kalahari the Bushmen doze out the heat in their grass nests under natural shade. When the heat is unusually strong they soak the grass of their beds with urine. They have no surplus water as the Biskra cafe owners have, but evaporating urine cools the ground just as effectively. That knowledge was useful to Mrs. Laura Scott when she, her husband, and her six children were stranded in a desert canyon beyond Moab, Utah, some years ago. They soaked their clothes with urine. Its evaporation cooled their bodies and saved their sweat. Despite old desert-survival stories, evaporation for cooling is the only intelligent use for urine or seawater in a water shortage emergency.

American mechanics at Wheelus Field, Libya, told me that they, like the native population, went to work at 5 A.M. and quit at 11 A.M. "If we can't get the day's work done by then," they said, "we come back at 5 P.M. During the midday you just can't work efficiently. You can't pick up a metal tool without burning your fingers, and some men have been hospitalized with burns from touching a plane's wings in the heat."

Experimental physiologists have found that a man working in 110° F. heat is 25 percent less efficient than he is in cooler air. I was glad the mechanics didn't work in midday heat on any plane I had to ride. That 25 percent lower efficiency could result in a careless mistake which the pilot might not discover until we were halfway to Timbuktu.

Where man has adjusted his activities and his needs to the natural rhythm of the desert or semi-desert, his life has not been too hard. The Plains Indians of America completely changed their agriculture-hunting way of life when the Spaniards brought horses to America. The horse gave the Indians mobility to follow the rhythm of buffalo migrations. They could live on bison meat, build shelters of bison hides, and even make boats of hide when they needed water transportation. With horses to follow the wild herds the Indians living on the edge of the Great Plains gave up planting seeds and harvesting crops for the free, nomadic life of more arid lands.

Before the white man came, Pueblo people lived in the arid lands from Nevada deserts to the plains of Texas. They cultivated corn, beans, tobacco, cotton, and other plants, despite the uncertain rains. Like the Egyptians they depended largely on seasonal floods to water their fields. Agriculture was reasonably productive when beaver dams helped control the floods. The people of some villages went en mass to hunt the buffalo. Others supplemented their food crops with antelope, deer, and rabbits. They also gathered yucca and cactus fruits. Some of them still go into the piñon country to collect the little piñon nuts.

The Rancheria tribes, including the Papago and Pima of southwestern Arizona, were farmers too, but they depended almost as much on wild foods as on their crops. Although the groups lived in fixed villages they moved from one area to another following the rhythm of the desert seasons. Mesquite beans, cactus and yucca fruits, acorns and piñon nuts, roots and rhizomes of grasses are just a few of the natural foods they used. Someone has said that because they worked *with* the desert six hundred Papago could live in an area where sixty whites would starve.

In ancient Egypt the rhythm of the desert was recognized. The Bible relates how Pharaoh put Joseph in charge of all Egypt to see that surplus from seven years of bumper crops was stored against the famine of seven years of poor harvests which were to follow.

When I first went to North Africa one of the French colonists tried to get me to invest in either sheep raising or wheat farming. That was a poor year and I was skeptical. I told my friend frankly that I didn't believe his advice. "After all," I said. "I have seen sheep starving and huddled against the straw sacks to keep from freezing. Losses will be heavy this year."

"Of course they will," he answered. "Nature provides just enough. Man is the glutton who wants his own way rather than conforming to Nature's way. If you come here with capital enough to last you ten years and operate your fields intelligently you can retire comfortably. During any seven-year period there will be at least two years of complete failure. You won't even get your seed back then. Some years you'll break even or get a little profit. During the usual cycle there will be a couple of profitable years. You'll make enough to cover your past losses. Then there will be one *bumper crop* to make you rich."

My friend is right, but his wisdom includes a thorough knowledge of arid zone natural history and a seven- to ten-year plan for cooperating with the desert. In poor years he'd curtail his operations, reduce his flocks, and give the survivors the best care possible. In good years his strong females produce more and healthier young, just as do the Gambel's quail of Nevada.

Not many will follow such a plan. Man tries to standardize production instead of "rolling with the desert's punches" and waiting for the favored season as the desert quickies do. So the bison were "harvested" for their tongues and hides, the good meat left for crows and scavengers. Beaver pelts became felt hats and Indian agriculturalists had to abandon productive desert gardens. High prices for wheat made dust bowls where once the buffalo roamed. Farmers plowed up more grasslands to plant more wheat and take advantage of the high prices.

Then came the drought. Plowed land, unprotected by native grasses, dried to dust and was blown away.

Everywhere the story of the desert is similar. Once a Mongol could mount his horse in the eastern Gobi, ride it till tired, turn it loose in a herd, and mount a fresh animal. Riding on "the lasso relay" he could cover a thousand miles and return by a different route, certain that each herdsman would recognize the strange horse in his herd and return it to its owner. No longer is the Gobi free like that. Now there are boundaries to each principality, each prince has customs collectors, and herds can't move so readily to greener pastures.

Once Arab camel herds followed the green grass north across the desert with the spring and returned on drier forage to their winter range. There was no overgrazing on so wide a pasture. In the Sahara a similar pattern once prevailed. Nomads of the south grazed their camels north to help the sedentary natives harvest grain. In later years such migrations slowed to a trickle. The open range was closed to nomads by overgrazing local flocks of sheep and goats. Today there's no room for the nomad herds in the north. Now they are forced to become farmers or move to the cities.

As I write, a copy of *African Wildlife News* is on my desk. "Elephant Damage on the Increase," a headline says. What has elephant damage to native vegetation and to agriculture got to do with survival in sun and sand? Once the elephants followed the natural rhythm of the vegetation. As waterholes dried up they moved on to other pastures and other waterholes. An adult male elephant requires twenty to thirty gallons of water per day. In Tsavo National Park, Kenya, man has introduced artificial waterholes and elephants are on the increase. Water is available. Elephants are no longer forced off the drying pasture into their former seasonal range. Deforestation of the elephant range and increased cultivation has crowded the big animals into the national parks, but available water makes it easy for them to avoid their natural migration.

In the Sahara and North Africa we know there has been no significant change in the rhythms of the rains nor in the volume of average rainfall. Why then the change from Rome's "Granary of Europe" to marginal agriculture over so much of the area?

Certainly modern plant ecologists, animal biologists and anthropologists, the students of desert peoples all know more about how to make efficient use of arid lands than the Romans did two thousand years ago. But that knowledge is not now the wisdom of the people or of governments of the people. In some places in the world, notably Arabia, Israel, and portions of the U.S.A., scientific knowledge has been put to use in a sensible manner. But much education of people and of the various departments of their governments must be done before production can approach the natural capacity of desert lands. When that cooperation and understanding between scientist, desert dweller, and their various government departments becomes real, then the arid lands again will be efficient grazing plains, as they were when the buffalo roamed and prospered in harmony with the desert's rhythm.

Arab sheiks and desert hills near Djmila, Algeria. When Rome ruled the world, this general area was the "Granary of Europe." Overgrazing, not a change in climate, has denuded this once beautiful grassland.

AUTHOR'S PHOTO

Desert rains cause real damage even on a gentle slope in the Gobi Desert when overgrazing keeps the native grasses too short and sparse to check the flow of rainwater.

AUTHOR'S PHOTO

INDEX